Men for Others

Men for Others

by STANLEY J. ROWLAND, Jr.

The missionary has come to join others
in their home, that in it Christ may find
his dwelling place.
     —D. T. Niles, Ceylonese theologian

FRIENDSHIP PRESS
NEW YORK

COPYRIGHT © 1965 BY FRIENDSHIP PRESS, INC.

LIBRARY OF CONGRESS CATALOG CARD NUMBER: 65-11439

PRINTED IN THE UNITED STATES OF AMERICA

To my fellow missionaries

Contents

Men for Others

· 1 ·

The Two Missionaries

THE lights were going on as they walked leisurely along the narrow street, the stubborn old man with his thin shock of white hair and his youngest son, a lanky hospital intern in tan slacks, brown loafers, and a white shirt buttoned neatly at his wrists. The air was cooling, the heat of a humid June day rising from the pavement. Half a block away, from the doors of a coffee house, the melody of "Blues in the Night" came tinkling from a slightly metallic-toned piano.

"How about it, Dad? This is where that poet reads." The young man had stopped, hands in his pockets, and was looking down at his father with a somewhat tentative grin.

Beneath the pleasant voice and grin, the old man sensed the same shout for recognition that had come from his son the time he first climbed a tall cedar in their yard in Iran. Now the old man said, "Sure, boy, I'll join you."

They walked together to the dim, noisy coffeehouse. It was not easy for the old man. He had always regarded such places as a sinful waste of time. He had first learned this from his parents and preacher, back on the Iowa farm, and he had never been in a cafe that offered entertainment. He had been in Paris at night with his wife and strolled with her for an hour on the Champs Elysées. During the nights they had spent in Teheran, he had used the time as a precious gift that let him study the medical journals for the latest developments. His wife had moved their household four times in their first six years, traveling by donkey cart, and she had rarely known whether he would be home for dinner at night. She had borne five children, one of whom had died of cholera when the missionary was on a tour of the villages. He had returned to bury the child, spend half an hour with his wife, and then go into the dispensary, where fifty people waited with ailments ranging from infected hangnail to advanced cancer. His wife had died ten years ago, and he had buried her beside the child in the little cemetery. Most of all, he remembered her patient smile.

In Iran he had removed a bullet from a boy's neck on a kitchen table by firelight, while a revolt flamed and sputtered in the streets outside. He had operated on a princess, making it possible for her to have children, and with the same deft care he had delivered the babies of some two thousand village women, peasant women, and beggar women. With an eye operation, he had given sight to 1,500 people. He had operated by candlelight and once by torchlight in a tent, for years by the light of kerosene lamps, their flames a yard away from the explosive ether.

Finally, for the past ten years, he had worked in the tile and chromium room of the modern hospital he had built from the ground up. It was one of the first in Iran, and he had left it in the hands of young Iranian doctors he had helped to train. They were good; they could carry on well. This thought had given him solid satisfaction when he had signed his retirement papers that afternoon and heard the door click shut on the treasurer's office, and with the click forty years of his life seemed to fall from his shoulders like a loose hospital gown.

But he had failed with his young son. This thought went through his mind as he sat at the wooden table beside the little stage in the cafe. Though the boy was becoming a doctor, he had evidently abandoned his loyalty to the Master Physician, and had written his father a letter ridiculing religion. The ridicule had hurt all the more for being sophisticated and half-disguised.

The waiter brought a cup of expresso coffee for his son and Turkish coffee for him and set these on the bare wooden table. Turkish coffee, with its strong sludge and smell of the Orient! He didn't know it could be bought in New York. His son paid, and the prices were twice what they should have been. The people at the other tables were evidently paying the same prices, though they looked as though they had little money. Some of the men had beards and lisping lips, and some of the girls were dressed in blouses drawn tight across their breasts, while others had long hair and wore baggy wool sweaters, despite the warm weather. The place smelled of cigarettes and sweat. His common sense as a doctor told him that there were some very unhappy people here, while his conscience repeated that the dim cafe was an expensive and sinful waste of time.

But he reminded himself firmly that in Iran he had done things, for the sake of his work and call, that went against his grain. This was for his son.

A fairly young man, in a loose jacket and tieless shirt, stepped onto the platform for a moment and casually announced a poet. "This is the one I want you to hear, Dad," the young intern remarked. The poet came to the stage from a side table. He seemed very young, a trim lad dressed in tan slacks and a black turtle-neck T-shirt. He carried a loose leaf notebook, which he opened and held before him.

"The Blasted Christ," he announced. The piano took an insistent, jazzy beat, and the poet began to read.

Christ was being mocked. Christ was being kicked and blasted through the streets by teen-agers and streetwalkers and men with ivory Cadillacs. His son's letter had contained ridicule. But this?

"It's sacrilegious," the old man said numbly.

"Yes. It was the first time," his son replied.

"Boy, what are you trying to tell me?"

"Listen."

The poet was reading:

> We tossed him in our trashy streets,
> and hit him with our cool sports cars
> that carry refrigerated girls,
> and then he blessed our bitter tears.

Blessed? "Father, forgive them. . ." the old man thought, remembering the familiar Bible verse. The poem seemed like the crucifixion all over again. The poet stopped, and turned the pages of his book.

The old man poured his coffee, and as he did so he looked at his steady fingers, long and deft, and again he remembered. It was the fingers, working as a smooth extension of his mind, that had felt for the tumor on the intestines, felt for the bullet in the boy's neck, felt the infant as it breeched to life, and his mind always kept saying, "give life, heal life," and his fingers had obeyed. He had done it because his own life had been deeply renewed and made purposeful when he had steadily given himself to the Master Physician, the same one whom the poet was having run over by sports cars—"cool" sports cars. The old man wondered if the temperature had some significance. The poet had started again, his voice raised above the jazzy piano notes.

> If I speak in the tongues of statesmen and movie
>   stars,
> but have not love . . .

The old man couldn't think anymore. It was so familiar, yet so utterly new. He simply sat, rather numbly he thought, and listened. The poem was like a parody, and it ridiculed parts of modern life. But the more he listened the less like a parody it seemed, and the more the old man felt a deeper rhythm of joyous laughter in the reading. As poem followed poem and the old man sat, listening dumbly, he felt a common theme, a theme composed of slashing ridicule and the run-over Christ, strange deaths that were died in streets and dim cafes, and then this laughter that began bubbling from the very deep of things.

Now the poet was concluding, speaking from memory, his face direct and gaunt in the spotlight, and his words riding over the piano notes of a tune that the old man almost recognized. And the poet was saying:

> Peace, I give to you.
> This peace, I leave with you.
> Not as our cars and foam rubber give,
> But the peace we are given from the bright deeps.

The poet stepped down toward their table, people began getting up at some of the other tables, and his son was standing and introducing the poet. The old man felt the poet's firm handshake and heard him saying warmly, "Doctor, I'm so glad to meet you at last." Then other people were talking with him and he was drawn away. A few minutes later, as they left the coffeehouse, the old man saw the poet sitting with a morose young man and a stringy-haired girl who was evidently the man's wife, to judge by the wedding rings the two wore.

"He's a help to them," his son remarked. "He's quite a good missionary."

"What? He's what?" the old man blurted and plunged through the door. Then the fresh air of the street hit him, almost like a cool shower, and they began to walk slowly. "A good missionary," his son repeated. "I've told him something about you and he admires you." Then the boy said, "He's the one who finally stripped me of phoney religion, and let me find a solid faith."

The words crashed into the old man's mind. He tensed at first, and the words were like a lightning flash that illuminates the new arrangement of an old garden, and ever afterwards the new arrangement is etched in the mind. The first poem *had* been like the crucifixion all over again, in a modern city, because that was the point. The second poem *had* been full of slashing satire, delivered from the perspective of the Cross. And there had been that undertone of joyous laughter, bubbling up like the resurrection. It was not religious, in the usual sense. It was Christ in the midst of man's turmoil, as it had been the first time. So *this* was what the boy had been trying to tell him. This was what his letter had been groping to say. This was what the poet had been saying, and saying it bluntly and lucidly.

"It's okay, boy," the old missionary said, exhaling a long breath. "It just took me awhile to recognize my own language." Then he began to laugh for no reason he could think of, but just laughing in a deep chuckle for no reason except that he suddenly felt very free and very much part of the night city, part of the young couples strolling in shirts and jeans, part of the dim piano music that followed them and the remembered words of the poet, part of his mission and the people in Iran and the two couples who were hailing a cab at the corner, and most of all he felt a father to his son.

It was sometime later that the old missionary and the poet had a chance to meet, and the old missionary slowly revealed his thoughts. In him, the young man saw one of the "fighting angels" of the older generation, tough men who had "heard the call" and gone overseas. By pouring their energies into a singleminded purpose, they had taken Christianity almost everywhere and had built most of the modern medical and educational work in underdeveloped lands, and they had done it largely in the space of two generations. There had been some casualties, notably among women and children; but they had done the job. In the poet, the old doctor was looking at a missionary who had "heard the call" and gone back into his daily situation. With his poetry, in the cafe he frequented, he expressed his experience of God.

As they talked across a table at the later meeting, the old man and the youngster found that they often used different references for Christ. To the old doctor, Christ was the Master Physician, which was in keeping with the doctor's work and way of knowing. To the young man, Christ was the center of inspiration, which was in keeping with his poet's work and way of knowing. For both, Christ was functioning as "the Man for others." He personified God's love in and for the world. The old man and the youngster had given themselves to this, and had become "men for others."

They didn't simply live "good Christian lives"—lives helped by faith, churchgoing, and things religious. Rather, they lived missionary lives: They poured themselves into their daily situations and work, giving of themselves, so as to transform people and things with "the mind of Christ"—with the love he personified. This, they helped each other realize, was the common denominator between them, and is really what mission means. It means joining with people and working with affirmative love, in the coffee shop or in Iran, so as to transform people and situations with the love exemplified by Christ.

The old doctor and the young poet did this with daily,

practical self-giving that was affirmative and redeeming. The young man and the older one had no illusions about high effectiveness. They did what they could, and found their talents increasing as they used their lives with the thrust of transforming love. They were missionaries, men for others.

While he talked to the doctor, the poet found himself increasingly interested in what made a man like this old missionary tick. The older man found himself challenged and refreshed, and teased with an idea: a new project he could start, with the help of the poet. He shaped the idea in his mind, diagnosing its possibilities carefully, until they had finished their coffee and time was running out. Then the old man said, "I think you may have a call with the church." He saw the poet's eyes dart over him, and his face become skeptical, yet still friendly and open. "I mean," the doctor said, groping for other words to say the same thing, "I think there is something you can give."

The poet relaxed. It was a problem of communication of old terms that didn't say much to him, the poet realized, and new terms that were still undefined.

"I've been speaking in some churches around the country," the doctor went on, "and I've had good turnouts and good interest. Yet there seems to be something that. . . ." He was groping now, trying to diagnose his impression. ". . . something that isn't moving, something more that should be happening. And you have a fresh perspective, a different way of seeing things, compared with old hands like me. Why don't you look at us? Write about the mission as you see it?"

The poet felt a quick, clear surge of interest. He could

get at people, at their *real* lives, not the promotions and speeches.

"After all," the old man was continuing, sensing the poet's interest, "the early Christians did this. Look at Paul's letters to the church in Corinth."

"You mean, write some magazine articles, or a book?" the poet asked.

"Something like that."

"I've done quite a bit of prose. It helps pay my rent. Poetry doesn't earn enough to keep my roaches alive."

"Very well," the doctor said, feeling efficient, moving now with his ingrained sense of discipline and order. "If you can come with me tomorrow, we'll go and talk with some people. Perhaps we can work out something. You know, I wish you could have met John Hayes. He was my generation, one of the great ones."

"You knew him well?" the poet asked.

"No, I only met him twice. Once was . . . "

The poet was interested. What did this Hayes fellow have that made such an impression? The old doctor was going on about him, and finally the poet said, "Look, I'd like to hear more. But before we go further, I've got to feel that I'll be free to write about people as I see them."

"You will have to be," the doctor said slowly and firmly, "because that is the only way you can bring us a fresh perspective."

· 2 ·

The Son of Lao Shih

AFTER two weeks of talk with committees that seemed to work like revolving doors, the poet got an assignment. He would start with the older, accepted ideas of mission and move toward the new.

So now he was in a sound studio at the Interchurch Center, listening to the recorded words of John D. Hayes, the name that had struck fire in almost every talk the old doctor had arranged. And the words of Hayes sounded formal and almost tritely cheerful. But a trite person didn't strike fire in the minds of men. If he had only met the man!

However, the former China missionary had died some years before. The poet had simply the voice of Hayes, a recorded radio broadcast in which the missionary discussed more than two years in a Japanese prison camp with 1,800 other people during World War II. The whole discussion gave not one fact about Hayes, except by inference. He talked entirely about others, giving credit to priests, teen-agers, prison baseball teams, a banker who carried 150-pound bags of flour, and butchers who could distinguish edible donkey and camel meat from rotten meat.

Now the voice was saying, "Achieving a happy, free life in the confines of a prison camp is something that we in America are best prepared to understand . . . "

It took a special sort of person to talk about freedom and happiness in prison, especially when his own father had died in the prison, as the poet's notes indicated. John Hayes sounded rather like an existentialist, a person who had affirmatively chosen his life and realized his freedom under harsh conditions—except that he wasn't talking about *his* life and freedom. He was talking about others, always others.

Through the glass window that separated him from the control room, the poet watched the Oriental girl change the record. This was another recorded radio interview, made after John Hayes had been imprisoned by the Communist Chinese.

"And now tell us, Dr. Hayes . . . "

A moment later the poet sat up suddenly, startled. The voice of Hayes was noticeably deeper now, with a resonant and compelling quality. He still spoke only about others, focusing on the Americans captured by the Communists during the Korean war. He called for love and understanding toward the prisoners. "They have had one way of life hammered at them, for months or even years. It will take a little while before they overcome this and are themselves again. It is hard for us to imagine the real, *physical pain* that one endures . . . " His voice had a note of personal intensity with these words. A few minutes later, he again referred to physical pain, and again there was the personal note. He had known pain under the Communists, the poet reflected, and had emerged as a stronger person.

During the following weeks, the poet talked with several who had known John Hayes. He read magazine articles, and talked at length with his widow, Barbara. She was a tall, energetic, and warm person, quick as a bird in some of her manners. From all these sources, the poet put together a picture of John Hayes—of what John Hayes meant to him, as he came through the lives of others. He couldn't put his pencil on anything definite, and say, "This defines the character of John Hayes," or "That is what John Hayes has left to posterity." It was the opposite.

A young missionary offered the clue. He was a field man, just as John Hayes had been, and when the poet asked this young field man what exactly he did, the missionary replied:

"Well, I talk with students and older people, discussing religion or their problems, like family trouble, or school, or crops. I'll check on our projects, like education or aggie (agriculture), or see if we need to start a self-help project. I just keep seeing people and sort-of talk."

John Hayes had specialized in "sort-of talk." His way of working contrasted exactly to that of the monarch of whom Shelley wrote in *Ozymandias,* a man whose fallen statue, "that colossal wreck" in the lone sands, bore the inscription "My name is Ozymandias, king of kings." To

John Hayes, life meant people. People were there to be met and brought together. Situations were there to be changed. He lived entirely in the present, responding to human need, and had a flair for responding in ways that were fun. But he had little flair for keeping records or for building with bricks and mortar. The work of John Hayes, like that of many missionaries, consisted mainly of something that people absorbed, the way plants soak up the rain.

John David Hayes was born on February 23, 1888, in a brick house in the missionary compound at Tengchow, China. He was the oldest son of the Rev. Watson M. Hayes and his wife, who went to China from the farming community of Greenfield in western Pennsylvania in 1882 to work with an older missionary in a college he had started in the city of Tengchow in Shantung Province in the north of China.

In time, this man from the farm earned the title of Lao Shih, or Old Teacher, a term of the highest respect. The Chinese typically reserved it for their own best scholars. Lao Shih, with his college and the textbooks he wrote or translated, helped greatly to instill in the Chinese the knowledge and thirst for progress that played a major role in producing the modern revolution. This revolution was almost the death of Lao Shih's son John.

John, the older of two brothers, grew up as the son of a missionary who was becoming a high official. He played with Chinese children, and like his father he acquired a Chinese sense of *p'ai t'ou*, a far-reaching term that the poet found impossible to render exactly. Roughly, it meant a person's sense of his position, his responsibilities, and the way he lived and carried himself. It meant his ability to do exactly the right thing, for a person of his standing, in each instance. The elder Hayes had a Chinese feeling for *p'ai t'ou* and became respected in a society that kept most Westerners at arm's length. At the same time, his wife preferred menus derived from the Pennsylvania farm.

John partook of both. He was exuberantly American. At the age of three, when he visited the family homestead in Pennsylvania, he bounced in a sweater and overalls through the fields as though he was on familiar territory. Once he was found driving the sow and her brood out the gate into the fields. At another time his family found him exploring a neighbor's sugar camp, and on still another occasion he tried to rout a swarm of bees from a cider mill. The bees won, and John came banging home through the hedges, flailing the humming insects from his brush of hair and shouting, "beeth! beeth!" But he went out again the next day. To this three-year-old, fences were something to get over and hedges were there to break through.

Years later, his mother shook her head and remarked simply, "John always had a way with hedges." Yet, from his boyhood through the rest of his life, he was like "a fish slipped back into water" whenever he returned to China. He grew in his father's faith, though he was more liberal in outlook. His faith gave him an inner security that let him feel at home on this continent or that. He could come into a place, join with its ways, take on its colors, and use these for his own ends.

At seven, traveling by mule litter for a day and a half,

he was sent to a school by the sea at Chefoo. It was an English preparatory school, and hewed to the routine of cold baths, exercise, strict discipline, plenty of Latin and Greek, and a strong sense of honor and right conduct.

John readily took on the customs of the school, and used one of these to show his exuberant American streak. Boys and girls were rigidly segregated after age ten. On Sundays, they were customarily marched in separate lines to church, more than a mile away. John managed to become leader of the boy's line, and twice crashed it into the girl's line. He also became head prefect his senior year, and was graduated with the school's good conduct watch.

From Chefoo he had come to the United States and Wooster College, where his cry was no longer "beeth! beeth!" but "girls! girls!" They had liked him, an enthusiastic young man who knew where he was going: into the mission field. The vocation had formed in his mind from the earliest time, and he never doubted it. He never felt himself perfect or too sinful for the work, never made it the occasion for a posturing piety, and never strove for abstract standards of holiness. He was always and irrevocably himself: warm, delightfully cockeyed at times, and always bubbling on from the inner springs of his life.

In his senior year . . . and the poet blinked in surprise, then shuffled through the papers on his desk. The records went all crazy. In his senior year John entered Princeton University, yet played varsity football for Wooster. He played basketball for Princeton, was graduated from Princeton, and promised his father that he would study at

Princeton Seminary. Then he won a Rhodes scholarship as a candidate from Wooster and set sail for England. The poet, who had once gotten into trouble for cutting a mere class, looked at the record of John Hayes and laughed himself limp.

At Oxford, John became very British. He always dressed with a flair, and now he joined a diversity of clubs, from the liberal Fabian Society to the conservative Oxford University Union. The latter debated such questions as "In the opinion of this house, Columbus went too far." John especially enjoyed the Leander Rowing Club, and ever afterward he frequently wore the flaming, salmon-colored scarf that distinguished Leander members. During his second year he captained the Merton College crew, and led it to a succession of victories. During a "bump supper," to celebrate the victories, the rowing shell was broken up and a section given to him.

At Oxford John met and courted Barbara Kelman, the daughter of a distinguished Scottish clergyman, who later was pastor of the Fifth Avenue Presbyterian Church in New York. Barbara gave him a picture of herself snapped on a day of misty sunlight along the Thames. It showed a tall girl, her smile slightly teasing, and her looks rather beautiful by any standards. After a meeting or two, John began to arrange "chance" encounters. Barbara related:

"I was walking along the Thames one afternoon, escorted by a young man . . ."

"Who?"

"I can't remember. But we were being chaperoned—a young woman always was, in those days—and here came John, striding along, with his head high, looking so full of life. He was wearing his white rowing blazer, with his salmon scarf tucked in casually. He simply came, and smiled with his flashing white teeth, and went along the path. But that finished me." Her eyes were a bit misty despite her staunch composure.

They were married later in her father's church in Edinburgh, and honeymooned in the Scottish highlands, where the heather was sweet and the northern summer daylight drowsed half through the night. As a marriage partner he was gay, curious, energetic, and restless.

"As a lover?" the poet inquired.

Barbara was reticent, and the poet understood. She had been raised in an older and repressive age, and dodged around this subject, though she left the clear impression that John Hayes had been as exuberant in this respect as in other phases of his life. Barbara was talking about the children now, and about their diseases and accidents. The poet saw that John could be insensitive in some ways. During most of his life, this man who was rarely off his feet, except to sleep, would look at a sick or injured member of the family and ask, "How did you do it, dearie?" He was deeply concerned, the poet felt from Barbara's discussion. Yet he didn't really understand. The illness seemed to him to be an absurdity, a mistake or accident in creation, wherein the child had inexplicably become involved.

John was graduated from Oxford in 1914, and started theological study at New College in Edinburgh. World War I had erupted on the continent, and John did some volunteer work with the Y.M.C.A. in France, where he was taken for British. After a season he rebounded to

England, where he continued his studies in Edinburgh. It was there that he and Barbara were married. After their honeymoon they sailed for America. Their first child, Margaret, was born here, and John in 1917 was graduated from Princeton Seminary, keeping his promise to his father. He was ordained, and sailed with his wife and baby on the "Empress of Japan," bound for China. Barbara, who'd had a sheltered upbringing, had to learn to care alone for the baby. The poet gathered that she did not have an easy time of it.

They arrived in Peking on a winter night of cold, clear moonlight. From the station, they went "bowling along the streets in rubber-tired rickshaws—bowling along in the moonlight. It was golden-white, and metallic in its brightness." They passed the moonlit roofs of the palaces in the Forbidden City—the innermost part of Peking— and went to the other end of the city, to their missionary home near the Drum Tower. Here the drums were beaten softly every night, to keep off the devils that were supposed to come from the north.

In the broad daylight of the following days, Barbara saw the poverty of the people, and noticed homeless children digging little homes—caves in garbage heaps. She was deeply shocked and unable to do anything. She couldn't begin taking children into their modest quarters, because they would bring brothers and sisters, a continual flood. Hence, some missionaries ran orphanages. Barbara's shock at human misery, subtly numbing, had stayed with her all the years in China.

After the first shock, she enjoyed active days with John that winter. On Saturdays they took long bicycle rides and came "fighting home against the wind with a kind of exultation." The baby was restless and kept her awake at night. Barbara worried and consistently had too little sleep. Yet she continued at the fast pace, living near the limits of endurance, a tall, slender, and lovely young woman who rode through the buffeting winds and kept pace with her husband. He had developed the strength of a wild stallion, and had the stallion's capacity to snatch rest as it suited him. This was not so for Barbara. With another year and another pregnancy, she began to have periods of depression.

John was unaffected. He "came and went like a meteor," she recalled. "I couldn't keep track of him. Nobody could."

The sort-of talk had begun. His professional biography showed an enormous list of activities, beginning with student work, which had evidently been his favorite. He also did flood relief and famine relief, taught languages, directed the Presbyterian mission in Peking for some years, advised half a dozen groups, and was involved in a tangle of special projects.

The more the poet probed, the more he saw how difficult it was to untangle the man's career, and how fruitless. "The impact of the man was much greater than the sum of his parts," a former associate of John's told the poet. He had worked in the Chinese way, doing a lot of things simultaneously, like someone knitting an incredibly complex and beautiful design that could never be defined by this thread or that. The poet turned up another estimation, this time from a Chinese businessman: "He is the ablest man I ever saw." He had the ability that counted most in China: the ability to work with people and get them working harmoniously together.

John brought the different relief projects together, which no one had done before. He insisted without ever seeming to insist, and changed minds without ever contradicting. His favorite phrase was "not only that, but . . ." and so he affirmed and made over a piece of work. He developed ecumenical student groups and played a real part in the movement for Christian unity. He had a way with hedges, the poet recalled.

On one occasion, when Barbara took a trip with him, she discovered that an hour's simple journey to a conference, and an hour's return, took them from breakfast until long after dinner. John wove around the route, visiting a school here, a village church there, a student group some place else, consulting, encouraging, and promising help or supplies for the needs he uncovered. They reached the conference, where John accomplished two or three things besides the stated objective, and then returned by another devious route, again visiting, encouraging, and helping. He accomplished things without seeming to push. The poet finally pinned down an example.

The Peking Police College requested classes in Christianity. Five dollars, given John by a visiting student, was enough to start the work. It was conducted by an "exceptionally intelligent" young Chinese teacher. Before long, they had seventy students in three classes. They learned about Christianity but also learned a simplified form of writing and elementary clerical skills. Then, as they became proficient, their skills were channeled into voluntary social service work, and into the teaching of others.

John kept the project snowballing, never seeming to push or demand, always encouraging the Chinese pastors to do the teaching or preaching they wanted to do, yet always moving the project along.

In 1920 there was a major earthquake. Barbara was sitting at the dining room table with the children and their nurse, early on a December evening in Peking. John was off somewhere. Suddenly, for no apparent reason, she started to feel seasick. Then the pictures on the wall began to sway, not sharply, but in long movements. A small stemmed vase fell over on the mantle, rolled, and fell to the hearth with a quick crash. That was all.

There was no damage in Peking to speak of. The vibration had not been sharp, but deep, almost majestic in an ominous way. They were feeling the shock from an earthquake a thousand miles away, to the northwest in Kansu Province. Its land and mountains were composed of loose soil, which crumbles easily.

At that moment in Kansu, also dinnertime, a large mountain topped by a temple collapsed into a valley. Great chasms opened in the earth, and swallowed whole camel trains. Other mountains split asunder and collapsed. The earthslides began, cubic miles of earth and trees rumbling at terrible speed. One roadway, bordered with poplar trees, rode a landslide for three quarters of a mile without damage to the road, the trees, or the bird's nests in the trees.

There were seven great landslides in the Valley of the Dead, as it came to be called. Every man, woman, child, and animal was killed, except for three men on a farm. The farmhouse, with its buildings and threshing floor, lay on a mountainside. As the mountain broke, the huge earth-slide carried the buildings and threshing floor along on its crest. It tumbled through the valley. The trees went under, and still the farm rode the crest of the gigantic slide. It rode right across the valley, was spun around, and came to rest on the side of what was left of another mountain. The farm was intact with its threshing floor, and the three farmers went back to their work.

The devastated area measured about 100 by 300 miles. Ten cities were smashed. Towns and innumerable villages went under. Some 200,000 people were killed. It was called "the day the mountains walked." And some of the earthslides from broken mountains rumbled right across rivers, damming them, and causing the threat of floods in the spring.

John Hayes got there, wearing his drab jacket and the dun-colored scarf that took the place of his Leander scarf during disaster work. His party to investigate the disaster included himself, a personal servant, and a Seventh Day Adventist missionary named Joseph Hall, who had a journalistic flair. They were to report on relief needs to the International Famine Relief Committee. They found hundreds of square miles that looked like the surface of a dead planet. It had been a well-defined countryside of mountains, valleys, towns, farms, and green trees. But the quake turned it into an undulating area of rock and dirt. Often John would ride for miles without seeing a single living person or animal or a single blade of grass. Deep beneath their path, whole villages were buried.

But John was not the only missionary in the stricken area. In a cluster of refugees, they found two American women missionaries. From Barbara's description, they sounded like the kind of plain, thin-lipped spinsters who seem quite unattractive when viewed from the cocktail table or the scholarly study. Yet here they were, living in a hovel made of dirt and mats, sharing and helping with all they had. John's party offered to help the women to better quarters, but they declined. They preferred, the women said, to share the hardships of the people they were trying to help.

In Peking that spring, while John was away, the wind blew from the depths of the continent, coming hot and dry and laden with brown dust. On one day Barbara counted seventeen buckets of dust that she and the servants swept up from the house. It came from the destroyed land a thousand miles away, where her husband was, and was carried on a hot wind that frayed the nerves and seemed to shrivel her. John returned in May, after outlining the relief needs and seeing work go into action. The committee threw hundreds of squads into clearing dammed rivers, distributing food to refugees, and trying to get an area the size of Pennsylvania into some sort of shape to support its surviving people. Many of these relief workers were missionaries.

It was probably, the poet reflected, the greatest and most underreported earthquake in modern times. In a *National Geographic* article, written by Upton Close, he found some clear descriptions of the damage. It was a neat piece of reporting. But it sounded, without saying so, as though Upton Close had been in the center of things. Actually, the missionaries had been in the center of things, with John Hayes placed in charge of the little party that reported on the damage, and with missionaries bearing the brunt of the relief work. Then why this report by Upton Close, reflecting upon Upton Close?

The poet investigated and did a slow burn. Upton Close had known about John Hayes and the work of the missionaries, because Upton Close was the pen name for Joseph Hall, the Seventh Day Adventist missionary who had accompanied John. How different they were! John worked expressively, pioneering for disaster relief, starting the police college, organizing student groups—and the work didn't reflect back on him, but developed its own momentum.

So John's work moved forward, with John dropping into the background and the work becoming a living part of history. He and Barbara summered in the East Cliff section of Peitaiho, a seaside resort some eight train hours from Peking. They had five children finally and occupied a big house that was a hub of activity. The resort was started by missionaries, and included Western business people and Chinese families, all on a completely equal footing. The Chinese and Westerners at this missionary resort swam together, attended concerts together, played tennis together; and it was good.

But back in Peking and other cities, there were green parks that sometimes carried the sign "No Dogs or Chinese Allowed." These were Western concessions, with Western laws and courts and Western troops—big hunks of the cities carved out and run by foreign powers. The situation was like cutting Central Park off from New York City and putting up the sign: "No Dogs or Americans Allowed." It was like having large sections of Chicago run by foreigners for foreign profits, with Chicagoans who entered any of these sections treated as aliens. The poet thought of these things as he walked the streets of his city, and he began to understand the rage that had slowly and deeply built up in the hearts of Chinese people. At this period, they were no longer hopeless and ignorant. Many had become educated, thanks to the work of men such as John's father, and they could imagine something better. They had learned to hope, and resented the plight of their land. A reckoning more severe than the Kansu earthquake was gathering force.

The war with Japan postponed the reckoning. The bombing of Pearl Harbor caught Barbara in the Philippines with their two younger children. They were interned, then repatriated, and joined the three older children who were studying in America. John was caught in Peking, where he was serving as chairman of the mission and president of the College of Chinese Studies. Before internment, he moved between Japanese and Chinese, building some bridges of understanding that made life a little easier.

In concentration camp, John's main job was to tend the oven. (He hadn't said a word about this in his recorded account, the poet reflected.) For long periods, he was on duty ten hours a day. Yet he found time to care for his parents, conduct morning prayers, and start a debating club. And he did a lot with his sort-of talk.

Concentration camp life caused some to despair, or scoff at Christianity, or fall into confusion. Some people, especially younger ones, began coming to the oven to talk to John. Standing stripped to the waist in searing light and grimy with sweat and coal dust, he would listen to their questions. "Where is God, anyhow?" "What has my faith got to do with this?" "How come this can happen to good Christians?" John listened mostly and responded from the depth of his own faith. What he said was apparently simple, and evidently carried the weight of conviction.

The trickle of people grew into a little group around the oven, and then into more groups. John kept stoking, never flinching from the ruddy heat, and always listening, then responding. A girl with strong suicidal tendencies came to him every day for a long time. Today, she is the wife of a missionary professor. In time some of the camp atheists came, at first to scoff, and then to listen to the discussion. As John continued with his listening and talk, the atmosphere of the groups changed and morale grew stronger. Two of the atheists rethought their beliefs, through long periods of difficulty, and later became Christian missionaries. John also changed in prison camp, becoming less restless, more firm and calm.

After World War II, John spent a year and a half as assistant pastor at the National Presbyterian Church in Washington, D. C. It was a good time for Barbara, and they were popular. John had become the kind of person who could enter a crowded room at a party, and without calling attention to himself, find that conversation was dwindling and people were drifting toward him. He and Barbara became beloved in Washington.

But China called again, and not through the mission board this time. He was asked by the Church of Christ in China to help with its work in Kweichow, in southern

China. He responded with alacrity, and he and Barbara set forth. They had seen poverty and starvation in Peking. But Kweichow was worse: "Poor, oh so wretchedly poor," Barbara remembered, and the poet felt a note of despair in her voice. John gaily set to work.

The Communists came in 1949, feeding on the poverty, resentment, and utter disorganization of China. They made noble promises and gave the country its first government in decades that could actually govern. John put Barbara on a plane to safety and stayed on the job. In time, the Communists accused John of subversive activities. On the other hand, John seemed to go along with the Communists, even attending indoctrination sessions.

The poet examined the material closely, and the truth slowly and clearly dawned upon him. John had dealt with the Communists in exactly the effective manner needed. He did not break with them or try to wall them off, which would not have worked, the poet knew, because walls never worked for very long. The Maginot Line had been overrun, and the Great Wall of China had been overrun repeatedly, and Goliath behind his wall of armor had been killed by the flexible David.

John befriended the Communists, and not in a crafty way. He befriended and joined with them sincerely, as individual human beings. "Love your enemies," the poet mused. Did it work? John joined a government school, becoming professor of English. He adapted to Communist rules, attended indoctrination sessions, and was on very friendly terms with the Communist organizer. He respected him as a person. And he continued to do a sincere, dedicated job of teaching English.

Yet, the poet realized, John wasn't the slightest bit inclined to communism. On the contrary, it was the Communists who had to watch out for him, wily and yet as innocent as a dove. He never questioned or opposed the fact of Communist government. From the depths of his faith, in each moment of life every day, he showed his strong respect for the dignity and freedom of each person he met. He lived his belief in the God-given dignity of persons. And this, of course, was subtly and profoundly subversive to Communist ideology and the whole Communist concept of man. The new tiger that controlled China had a thorn in its paw, and the name of that thorn was John David Hayes.

He thought in Chinese, spoke the language flawlessly, and lived his faith in a way that sowed disillusion and doubt in the minds of the Communists. As the poet got the picture, he wished there were ways to get a lot of American Christians into China to do as John had done. For example, at the end of an earnest tirade by a Communist indoctrinator, John might remark genially: "When the water goes down, the stones will be seen." It was an old Chinese proverb, and meant that the truth would emerge when the present torrent subsided. A mild remark like this, spoken from the heart of faith and precisely timed, sowed doubt in the minds of the hearers and left some tittering at the Communist speaker.

Everyone was encouraged by the Communists to criticize himself and turn informer. The students were divided, then organized into Communist groups, with the most zealous youngsters given leadership. Yet the Communists couldn't charge John with being indifferent or hostile to these students. He invited them indiscriminately into his home, a sincere friend to all. He let them talk, and quietly proceeded with his sort-of talk. Students were now "volunteering" time for indoctrination, and peasants, after some brief months of jubilation over their "release" and new power, were now "volunteering" crops and services. John could seem to go smoothly along with this in student discussions, but put an inflection to the word "volunteering" that cast doubt on the whole process and showed the cynical power behind the glowing promises of the Communists.

Propagandists disparaged the United States and praised Russia. John could readily adapt this. He could speak of missionaries from capitalist countries who merely fed and doctored the poor, compared with the way in which noble Russia recognized the true spirit of the Chinese Communists by giving them lethal weapons. With the Korean war, anti-Americanism went into high gear. President Truman was pictured as the "running dog" of Western monopolists who ground the people under their heel. The Communists pictured themselves as the true friends of the people. John praised these ideals of friendship, complimenting the Communists warmly on their interest in the "downtrodden" populace of the United States, and proposed that the Communists implement this friendship. He could suggest ways to start. The Communists declined, thus exposing the complete hollowness of their "friendship."

General MacArthur was withdrawn from Korea, and John quickly and quietly observed to others that it was perhaps the first time in history that a nation had withdrawn a winning general in the interests of peace. Several days later, when the Communist propaganda machine had formulated its line on the MacArthur withdrawal, it had to buck John's interpretation, which had become widespread in the university.

The shooting of landlords began. They were carried through the streets in the death cart—an old truck painted red—and forced to stand up before a crowd that was incited to shout "kill, kill." Communist agents were scattered through the crowd, and everyone had to seem enthusiastic or risk accusations and shooting. Nobody had the elementary right possessed by the most disadvantaged citizen of a Western democracy: the right to be silent or shrug his shoulders and walk away. After the crowd had screamed its sentence, the landlords were carted through the town to an execution place on the outskirts. Time was allowed for a crowd to gather. Schoolchildren were placed in the front row. Then the landlords were blindfolded, made to kneel, and shot at point-blank range from behind the head. Soft bullets were used, so that they would mushroom in the skull and destroy the face.

John arranged the schedule of his courses so that the students had to study and perform Shakespeare's *Merchant of Venice*. He suggested that this showed the struggle of Western people against oppressors. He pointed out the mean ways of the capitalist Shylock, how he actually tried to require a pound of flesh. Why, it could make a person bleed for days! He pointed out the terrible justice that the people meted out to Shylock, scarcely leaving him with his life and some property. And rehearsal after rehearsal, there was the recitation: "The quality of mercy is not strained, but droppeth as the gentle rain from heaven. . . . "

The contrast scarcely flattered the Communists and was too clear for even the most narrow zealot to miss. But John remained genial and cooperative, never openly differing on politics. Hadn't he been showing the students how Western people also suffered from capitalism? It was hard for the Communists to accuse John of anything, especially when he was so friendly and so sincerely interested in each of them as an individual. In spite of themselves, they knew they had a friend in John Hayes. Still, they made him drop *The Merchant of Venice* from the curriculum. There had been complaints from higher up.

The thorn in the tiger's paw began to be an infection. It hurt all the way to Peking, and the tiger growled. A demonstration against John was organized in March of 1951, and after that he was watched and restricted closely. On October 29, 1951, he was awakened early in the morning. Several soldiers stormed into the house and yanked him out of bed in his pajamas. John was pleasant, treating them as though they were Boy Scouts enacting a crazy play. They took him out to the yard. Thirty soldiers had been sent to take him. "My," John remarked quietly, in perfect and subtly teasing Chinese, "you come in great force. Are you afraid of one unarmed man of sixty-three?"

The soldiers laughed uncomfortably and did not look at one another. Then the young commander, a former student at the university, had John abruptly hauled back into the house. He had to be rearrested, so that pictures could be taken. Dawn had scarcely broken, and it was dark in the house. They put him at his desk, pointed a revolver at his head, and took a picture. They had used no light or flash bulb, John pointed out. Then he gave them some quiet instruction in photography. The young Communists felt foolish and angry. They had him get back in bed, then took another fruitless picture of him being yanked out again.

Then, still in pajamas, John was marched through the main streets. Some cadres ran ahead, stirring up a demonstration against another "imperialist dog" who had been caught. But John didn't adopt the proper dog manner. He strode along. His thirty-odd captors trotted to keep up with him. John's head was high, his face calm, and he held his wrist manacles in full view, whereas the pack of Communist soldiery brandished their guns and made ugly faces. The "demonstration" was a fiasco for the Communists. They changed plans, taking John over back roads to the jail in Kweiyang.

For two weeks he was kept in a small cell. Then at eight one night he was hauled before two judges, made to sit on a small stool, and forced to stare up at the judges, who were under bright lights. The hammering began. He was charged with being a spy, and operating a transmitting set that sent secrets to the United States.

As they hammered at him in shrill voices, John found that the "spy" charge was based on the fact that he came to China for the Presbyterians, and J. Edgar Hoover, F.B.I. chief, was a prominent Presbyterian, and a trustee of John's home church in Washington. The charge may have seemed logical to the Communists. They had no experience of democratic voluntarism: the countless voluntary organizations, not connected with the government, by which Americans help one another and people overseas. Also, with no understanding of the Christian faith, they couldn't understand John's self-giving—how he could be so tirelessly devoted to his work, so charitable toward others, so genuinely concerned for each person, and so willing to share his time and his home with the students.

John, they reasoned, had to be a spy. Hence, he had to be controlled by the United States government. The "connection" with the F.B.I. proved this to them. Therefore, he had to be doing such things as secretly transmitting information. So he had to have a secret radio transmitter. In short, the judges that John faced were quite possibly victimized by their own brainwashing.

They shouted charges at John, and he denied them. He was taken from his cell at odd hours of the day or night, forced to sit on a little stool under bright lights, and hammered at by piercing voices for four, six, or nine hours at a stretch. The judges seemed to be making random charges. But they were probably proceeding by their own kind of belief and logic. If John hadn't been a spy in one way, then he must have been a spy in another way. Hence, a radio transmitter had to be involved somehow. They kept coming back to this.

After about three weeks, with John weak from the ordeal, the confinement, and a bare subsistence diet, his mind became numbed. On his inner eye, he saw a friend asking him how to dispose of a radio transmitter. John became quite convinced of this induced hallucination. Once convinced, he took responsibility for the supposed transmitter and made a full admission, since he didn't want to implicate his friend. His admission of responsibility indicated to the Communists that they had been right in believing he was a spy. The trial ended after forty days.

John was kept in his cramped and solitary cell. From the depths of his faith, and with hours of calm and patient prayer, day after day, his wounded mind began to heal. Though he scarcely realized it, he was growing spiritually stronger. Then came a second trial, with thirty-five days of hammered accusations, though these were spread over a longer period. On July 18, 1952, his solitary confinement ended, and he was placed in a cell with four other missionaries.

John was made to write a confession. He was stronger and clearer in his mind now. His favorite biblical text had always been, "Be ye perfect. . . ." He knew he was not. But something had happened in his relation with God, some deeper communion that healed him toward perfection. Now he confessed in detail his failure to live perfectly as a Christian missionary. To describe his failures, he had to say what the Christian faith was, and why, and what it meant. So for sixteen pages, which was placed on the court record, he discussed Christianity, inferring its superiority to communism point by point. It soon became evident that the balance of the proceedings was subtly shifting.

When John next met his judges—six of them, now—he saw them with a stronger spirit and viewpoint. It occurred to him that they were rather like insecure children. They had forced him to speak in English, through an interpreter. But when the interpreter gave a particularly bad translation, John corrected him in flawless and chastening Chinese. The judges began to get confused. The interpreter was saying one thing, and John was saying another, making sly jokes. They shouted at John, then shouted at the interpreter, and finally in exasperation they dismissed the interpreter. The trial was continued in Chinese.

The judges kept hammering at John. Hadn't he conducted the funeral of a Nationalist Party man executed by the Communists? He had, John said, and told them the prayer of the dead man's daughter: "Heavenly Father, forgive them. They did not know my father. Give them, I pray, a real sense of justice, a true love of the people, and so may true peace come to this poor land."

The judges were silent. Then the president of the court ordered John returned to his cell. Within a few days they hauled him in again, and asked how John could consider himself a friend of the Chinese people, when he and his father had come to China from an imperialist country. John replied by telling the story of his father, the Old Teacher, and how he had spent his life serving and bringing education to the Chinese people. John spoke with color and conviction, in facile Chinese, holding the rapt attention of the judges.

There was an uneasy pause. Then the proceedings continued. The judges asked John if he was trying to pry China away from her great friend, Russia, and make her lean toward America. John stood, gaunt and serene in the light, and said quietly:

"China should lean toward no one. The Chinese people have a vast capacity for good. I would have you, since you ask, teach the Russians your ancient good manners, civilize them, and then be the bridge yourselves between the Eastern and Western worlds. You have the power, if you are independent, to do it." Once again there fell a dead silence. The judges shifted uneasily in their chairs. The trial had turned; John's accusers had now become the accused.

He was returned to his cell, where he was presented with formal charges to sign. He was accused of trying to disrupt the Chinese-Russian alliance, and fostering Chinese-American friendship. He was further charged with using his university post for this purpose, and of using his home and other means to influence students and Communist cadres to oppose major government policies: liquidation of landlords, and falling into step on the Communist line. The charges were true. John had done these things, and done them well enough to influence thinking and sow doubt. He was able to sign the statement with a clear conscience. Now, he thought, he would certainly be shot.

But he was not. It was the judges who were shot—five of them, he learned later—for bringing the "People's Court" into disrepute. A prison warden came abruptly into John's cell, and with as much face as he could manage, he told John and his cellmates that they were being expelled. This was on September 6, 1952. On a mild evening a couple of weeks later, they crossed the border into Hong Kong. John was wearing his Leander scarf, its salmon color dull from the years, but still cheerful and debonair. Now, he also wore a beard.

He had been a strong man when his experience with

the Communists began. He emerged a powerful man. He commanded no fortune, army, or executive desk. Yet he could capture people's minds by simply walking into a room. He was powerful within himself, in his faith and character. He drew people to him like a magnet, and held them with a word or gesture. There was nothing great about the words and gestures. It was the resonance of the man, living in communion with the loving God. People felt more alive and meaningful, simply by being near him.

Yet he was still an action man, a field man, restless to be moving and doing. He went to work in Indonesia, at the invitation of the church there, and took the new assignment with enthusiasm. He helped to start a summer work camp. He sparked the development of the Christian Normal College at Salatiga in mid-Java, which became a university. He was at it again, with his sort-of talk, his efforts always pointing forward and developing their own momentum.

On his sixty-ninth birthday (seventieth by Chinese count, and a great occasion) some students gave him a big surprise party. Three days later he was driving in his Land Rover to Jogjakarta. Ahead, on the narrow road, he saw a boy on a bicycle.

The boy fell suddenly in front of him.

John swerved to avoid the boy, reacting instinctively. There was a sharp jolt, and his Land Rover flipped over in the ditch. He was taken unconscious to a nearby hospital. Shortly thereafter, a telegram to the United States contained this passage: "Indonesian friends making tremendous expression of affection sorrow. Mayor Salatiga vice-mayor thirty students staff normal college traveled three hours offering assistance. School closed all day honoring his memory."

John Hayes died as a field man, by the reflex of compassion. He was buried in the Christian cemetery at Salatiga. At his funeral, the mayor, a Muslim, and the president of the city council, a Communist, spoke at their own request in appreciation of John. He had reached even them with his sort-of talk.

· 3 ·

Medicine Man of Words

It was a January morning of clear sunlight in New York, with an icy wind that blustered through the streets, bullying people at corners and snatching their hats. Overhead, the high jets whistled silver through the blue air. In lower midtown, where the air hammers beat their violent song of creativity on the macadam of Park Avenue, the poet walked toward an office building, carrying a tape recorder.

An elevator whisked him upstairs, and a minute later he was walking into the office of Eugene A. Nida, Ph.D., translations secretary for the American Bible Society, which translates, publishes, and distributes the Scriptures. Dr. Nida came briskly from his office, taking off his reading glasses as he came. He had bright blue eyes in his small face. He walked with the bounce of a spring robin, and physically he didn't seem much larger. They went into Dr. Nida's office, and Dr. Nida began to talk.

Medicine Man of Words

He grew two feet taller. He hadn't grown physically, the poet knew. He simply seemed to grow, because in his thinking and ways he is a big man. The poet was looking at one of the foremost scholars in the field of primitive languages, a man who has personally worked on 135 of these languages, a man in the prime of life who has traveled much of the inhabited earth in conveyances ranging from astrojet to donkey cart, who has been christened "medicine man of words" by one African tribe, and who in his spare time has written nine books, ranging from the highly scholarly *Morphology, the Descriptive Analysis of Words,* to the breezy and popular *God's Word in Man's Language.*

As the sound of the air hammers rattled against the windows, Dr. Nida began. "My job is like that of a trouble shooter." He stacked his feet on a spare chair next to a stuffed bookcase, and continued, "I go out and help the translator in whatever stage he's in. Sometimes he may need help in working out an alphabet. Sometimes he may have a complicated grammar with thousands of forms for a verb, and he needs to know how to handle this. In linguistics, we have techniques for analyzing words and phrases. Once we know the meaning of a few, we can get others more quickly, and then break a language down pretty fast to its basic structure.

"Still, some of the grammars can be pretty fierce." For example, he explained, there are the strange sounds, "like so many squeals, squeaks, grunts, pops, and hisses, with queer vowels added at the most difficult places." Dr. Nida was speaking like an enthusiastic boy, as though each "pop" and "hiss" were a special friend of his.

"Then there are the clicks," he continued. "The Bush-man and Hottentot languages have twenty different kinds of click sounds. And we have to get this noise into an alphabet. Then comes the grammar, which can be pretty complicated. In Bolivian Quechua, words of thirty-two letters aren't uncommon. Also, in this language it is possible to take almost any verb root and add more than 100,000 combinations of at least twenty different sets of suffixes and particles.

"On top of this, there is the complication of tonal patterns in many languages. Take the Mazatec Indian tongue in Mexico. It has four different registers of tone, and glides go up and down from one register to another. The word 'tho,' pronounced on the highest tone, means 'will go out.' When it's produced on the lowest tone, it means 'a gunshot.' In between, the other tones and glides give you different meanings. So these patterns are a complication.

"Now," Dr. Nida continued, lounging deeper in the chair and swinging his glasses gently with one hand. "*Now*, when you get the language, your troubles have just begun. There is the cultural factor. Obviously, the tribal cultures are different from ours, the minds of these people are geared a bit differently, and they are better than we are at certain things. They can be more astute in describing behavior. For instance, the Zulu tongue distinguishes 120 different kinds of walking. When you're translating, you have to be careful, or you'll say that Christ walked like a pregnant woman or like a dandy in tight clothes. A missionary in the Congo once spoke of John the Baptist 'crying' in the wilderness. The trouble was that the word he chose for 'crying' applied only to infants.

"On the other hand, the Cuicatec Indians of Mexico have one word for 'believe' and 'obey.' 'When you believe,' they said to us, 'doesn't that mean you obey?' You see, we're dealing with people for whom the religious life *is* life, not a theory, and the words we use in translating must be rooted in their daily experience.

"A lot of these peoples have acute perception. For example, the Malagasy-speaking people of Madagascar distinguish and name more than a hundred different colors. Or take the idea of being worried or troubled. The Uduks of Ethiopia think of worrying as 'shivering in the liver.' The Navahos of North America say simply, 'my mind is killing me.' This is a pretty accurate idea, as psychosomatic medicine is finding out." He recrossed his feet on the extra chair, musing silently for a moment, and then continued:

"You have to be especially careful with metaphors, or anything like that. Literal translations won't go. One chap in Africa tried a literal translation of the phrase, 'heap coals of fire on his head.' It got through all right. The people thought it was a fascinating way to kill someone. They'd never thought of it before. And here it was, approved in the holy book."

Dr. Nida chuckled and launched into the story of a missionary in the bush country of central Africa. The language work was unrefined, and Christian teaching still new. The missionary and several tribesmen had built a pleasant outdoor chapel, clearing the bush from beneath the taller palms on a hillside. They made a simple table and a wooden cross that was placed thereon. Everything was ready for the first service.

The people gathered, respectful and expectant. Their new white teacher, master of so many strange and attractive ideas, stood beside the table with his open Bible. For this first service, he chose an opening that was timely and traditional. Translating from his Bible into the tribal language, he boldly and solemnly proclaimed:

"Enter the kingdom of heaven!"

"That's what he thought he said," Dr. Nida exclaimed, looking downright merry. "But what he *really* said was, 'Go sit on a stick!' It took quite a while before the missionary got his service untangled.

"Then in East Africa," Dr. Nida continued, "an interesting thing happened to our familiar words, 'The Lord be with you, and with thy spirit.' As they came through to the people, they meant 'The Lord be with *you*, because we don't want him anymore!'

"So we have to be careful with literalisms. At various points, the Bible said that Jesus 'opened his mouth' and spoke. You look at one of these tribal tongues that is full of grunts, pops, and gliding sounds, and you can see why they're apt to ask, 'How did Jesus talk? It says he opened his mouth and spoke. How can anyone speak with his mouth open?' Then there is the phrase, 'it came to pass.' We found that one missionary in Latin America was having trouble because he used the phrase frequently, and in the tribal language it simply meant, 'something came in order to pass here.'

"In West Africa, one literal translation had Mary sitting on Jesus' lap, instead of at his feet. In Liberia, we found that the translation of one phrase in the Lord's prayer—'lead us not into temptation'—had been jumbled. So the people simply inserted a phrase that seemed logical to them, from their previous beliefs. We found they were praying, 'Do not catch us when we sin.'

"However," Dr. Nida added, "we misconstrue things, too. Look at the scene from Genesis, between Jacob and Laban, that called forth the Mizpah declaration: 'The Lord watch between you and me, when we are absent one from the other.' Originally, it was a case of two jealous, cheating men who were calling upon God to protect them from one another. But we have twisted it into a request for mutual blessings and benefits." His mouth flicked in his typical, quick smile.

"The point is," he continued more seriously, "you've got to know the cultures and find the right idioms in the different languages. For example, the Mazatec people of Mexico haven't an adequate word for 'miracle.' But they have a phrase that does very well: A miracle is a 'long-necked thing,' something that makes people crane their necks in wonder. Similarly, the Valiente Indians of Panama have no specific term for 'authority,' though they have a vivid idiom. When someone has authority, they say 'He is on the handle.' It means that he holds the handle of the hunting knife. He is in control. The chief is 'on the handle.' When we say that God has authority, we say that he 'is on the handle.' These Indians also have a picturesque phrase for our expression, 'hope in God,' which has become a bit hackneyed. They say 'rest the mind in God,' which has a beautiful suggestion of calm and confidence.

"Our term 'Comforter,' for the Holy Spirit—comforting and guiding us—is very difficult to render sometimes. For example, among the Karre people of Central African Republic, one missionary explained at length the work of the Holy Spirit, seeking the right word or phrase. Finally the people exclaimed, 'Oh, he's the one who falls down beside us.' They told the missionary that on long treks, the injured and tired straggle to the rear and finally collapse beside the trail, knowing that they will be killed and eaten by wild animals. If someone comes along and takes pity on them, helping them to safety, this saving person is called 'the one who falls down beside us.' So, in their idiom, the Holy Spirit is 'the One who falls down beside us.' "

Dr. Nida was about to launch on another story when the poet said, "Look, slow down, and backpedal a little; tell me how you got this way—and why."

"Well, I just grew this way," Dr. Nida said.

He was born in 1914 in Oklahoma City, the son of a chiropractor. He had one brother. When the young Dr. Nida was eight, the family moved to Long Beach, California. He attended Sunday school regularly, delivered papers, and watered lawns. He did some amateur carpentry and collected insects. He went on to earn A.B. and M.A. degrees at the University of California at Los Angeles. After taking time out for work, he obtained his Ph.D. in linguistics, awarded from the University of Michigan in 1939. He went to work for the Bible Society, first as an associate and then as translations secretary—"and here I am," he said.

"But Dr. Nida," the poet protested, "the whole thing

sounds so hometown, so Main Street, so doggone Boy Scout—"

"Yes, I was a Boy Scout," Dr. Nida added brightly. "I earned sixty-six merit badges." Then he described the family life of his youth.

"We used to sit around in the evening, just the family, and talk. We'd talk about my father's work, and about our church—my parents were strong members of The Methodist Church—and we'd talk about missionaries, and Christian living, and what my father was planning. . . ."

As he spoke, his mind shuttled from work, to faith, and back to plans and work again. His talents began to be visible as he spoke of boyhood enterprises.

There was his carpentry. "I spent my money for tools and wood instead of ice cream, and made stick figures and even some abstract designs." There was his insect collection, carefully ordered. This revealed a working interest in natural life, combining with his carpenter's interest in form and design. There was the summer he spent in landscape painting. Now his interest in natural life, and in form and design, were combining with a working interest in mood and color. Then there was his good-humored promotional flare:

"I sold vegetables one summer, and put up a sign across the road saying, 'Don't Look at the Other Side.' Of course, people looked. I sold more vegetables that way.

"Around this time I explored quite a few religious groups. I was strongly influenced by the Friends. Finally in 1939 I was ordained in the Baptist Church, and I started work. . . ." His mind was again shuttling from work, to faith, to work. Faith was serving as an open vertical. It was a way of self-understanding and a way of exploring. After a while his career fell naturally into place, organized around this vertical. His boyhood talents were transformed, integrated, and increased. He had sought first the kingdom, as it were, and kept working. His ordination as a clergyman, in today's perspective, didn't seem crucial to his Christian vocation as a linguist.

". . . share this Christian faith," Dr. Nida was saying. "In its work, this Bible Society has put scriptures into 1,181 languages as of 1962. Outside the Western languages and a few others, most of the world's languages had no written form. About 90 percent of the world's written languages have been put in written form by missionaries and Bible societies. Many of these are primitive languages in Africa, Latin America, and the Pacific islands. Together they add up to a great deal. We've put them in written form, and then the people usually want to learn the national language, and have their children educated. . . ."

A truth was emerging. This Dr. Nida, straight out of Main Street, America, was not only a scholar but a prime agent of revolution. With language work, he and his cooperating missionaries had transported hundreds of tribes —peoples occupying big hunks of continents—into the modern era with its winds of change. And they had done it with missionaries and Bibles, for the sake of their biblical faith. There was just one sticky question for many people: "Doesn't this missionary work upset the happier lives of tribal peoples?"

Dr. Nida brought both feet to the floor and leaned forward, his blue eyes sparkling as he spoke. "In the first place, the lives of these people aren't idyllic. That's a myth taken from the idea of Jean Jacques Rousseau, and it simply isn't true. No responsible anthropologist today is that naïve, even if he isn't sympathetic with mission work.

"The tribal peoples have lived in a great deal of fear, such as the fear of black magic. Sometimes they are afraid to own livestock. Among the Tzeltals of southern Mexico, the translators found that the people were afraid even to own a pig—someone might cast a spell on them. Sometimes the people are afraid to plant or harvest on certain days, because their dreams haven't been right or the moon doesn't look right. If this goes on for awhile, they can waste the fruits of a whole season—which has happened. Or they may be afraid to have too good a crop—someone will be jealous and cast a spell on them. These peoples have all the basic human problems that we have, compounded with superstition and black magic. Then there are interesting customs. For example, in East Africa, when a king built a house, it was the custom for him to lay the foundation by driving a post through a live slave."

In West Africa, he indicated, in the steaming jungles at Calabar Bay, the people murdered twins, and also buried babies alive with their dead mothers. Scottish missionaries came here in 1846. Very slowly, with the help of one of the chiefs, King Eyo Honesty, they were able to get their Christian teaching across to the people, and the rites of fear and murder subsided. They built a school, the now famous Hope-Waddell Training Institute. More than half a century later, from the high bush country, there came to this school a little boy named Ibiam, who was afraid of juju practices. Later, the poet met him.

"Moreover," Dr. Nida asserted, his sentences bouncing

along, "you must reckon with the fact that very seldom did missionaries get to these places before commercial interests did. Slave interests were all over Africa before Livingstone got there. In fact, he wanted to go into the heart of Africa to try to defeat the slave trade. Then there are the copper mining interests in Central Africa, where sixty to ninety thousand men are sometimes brought together in huge compounds for months at a time, without their wives. In effect, they are economic slaves. And you can see this pattern again and again, commercial interests —mining companies, quite often—disrupting the tribal patterns. The church is trying to do something constructive in these situations, re-establish family life and give the people something to live for.

"The commercial interests go further than we often realize," he added, launching into another story: "One time I was traveling among the Tarahumara Indians of Mexico, a group of about fifty thousand quite isolated and primitive, with only a few superficial signs of Christian influence. For all practical purposes, they were pagan. Yet in a cave up on a mountainside, where one of these Indians lived, I heard a click-click, click-click-click—and sure enough, there was a Singer sewing machine.

"Or look at the influence of the motion picture industry in Africa, Latin America, and across the Pacific in Asia, in the growing population centers. The industry has gone into these places, many times with pictures that cannot even be shown in the United States, and has given the people an entirely perverted concept, not only of what the United States is like, but of what the ideals of life should be like.

"They get the idea that the average American is rich, lazy, and immoral, and that American women particularly are very, very bad. And we are supposed to have set something of a standard, something of an ideal in the development of our country. The perverted concepts of us that these people are getting from the movies are a tragic thing."

His face was sober, and his expression took on a certain hardness. Then he continued, "Of course, I won't go to the other extreme and say that the mission has disrupted nothing and has been entirely right. Certainly we have made mistakes and done silly things—like the old idea of putting mother hubbard dresses on women. But the people often don't take this sort of thing as seriously as some anthropologists make out." Then he described an incident on one of the Micronesian islands of the South Pacific. The poet drew him out with questions, and reconstructed the scene:

The service was about to begin in the island chapel, one of the little gems of simple and functional architecture that are sometimes found. A roof thatched with woven fronds was supported by slender, straight, gray tree trunks. Adobe walls, glowing ruddy in the sun, rose two thirds of the way to the overhanging roof. They let the air circulate freely while protecting the interior from wind and rain. Like some of the early Puritan chapels of New England, it was furnished with benches made of split and smoothed logs, a lectern, and a communion table with a plain wooden cross.

The women began coming to the service, groups walking in single file along the jungle trails to the chapel in its palm-studded clearing. Their posture and bearing were superb from years of carrying bundles on their heads. Their walk was measured and limber, and their bodies, completely naked, became ruddy chocolate as they caught the sun of the clearing. Each woman carried a colorful, carefully-folded bundle of light cotton cloth on her head. Instead of entering the chapel at once they went into the bushes.

There they took the bundles from their heads. These turned out to be mother hubbards, that old symbol of the superficial in missions. The women put on their mother hubbards and went into chapel with the men. After the service was over, and the women had greeted the visiting Americans, and had been duly photographed for the latest publicity blurb on mission work, they went back into the bushes, took off their mother hubbards, folded them onto their heads, and serenely walked home.

"I think there is a tendency to exaggerate this silly side that missions have sometimes shown," Dr. Nida remarked with a big grin. He leaned back in his chair, gazing for a minute out the sunny window behind the poet, and said, "Personally, I'm thrilled by some of the independent churches that have grown up among tribal peoples.

"For example, next week I'm going to spend a few days in the Otomi Indian community, not far from Mexico City. About two thousand people there have developed a most remarkable community with about twenty churches spread out over the valley. We didn't tell them what to do, or even try. *They* have brought the gospel to bear on every aspect of life, and their whole life has been transformed—from one of tribal jealousies and hardship to something loving and prosperous. They own land in common, and they have developed cooperative industries such as rope making. Politically, it is a kind of democratic theocracy, quite informal. The church is at the head of things, and settles all the problems. It is run by a pastor and the elders, who are elected. Obviously, tribal patterns have changed. But I call this more of a liberation and a fulfilment than a disruption."

"What about your wife?" the poet asked.

"She's theologically trained, and she goes with me as my assistant on a lot of trips. We have no children," and for the first time his face showed a trace of sadness, like a shadow behind his blue eyes. Then, slowly, the poet pried from Dr. Nida the fact that he gives his wife Toni home permanents in the steaming jungles, and she makes sure that he takes his anti-malarial pills. Their home is in nearby Westchester, Dr. Nida said, where they are members of North Baptist Church in Port Chester.

"I have a workshop," Dr. Nida continued, "and I make things like furniture, and abstract designs. And in between times I write articles on linguistics for magazines in this field, and. . . ." His cup runneth over, the poet mused, then asked:

"How many languages can you speak or read yourself?"

"Actually," Dr. Nida replied, "my work as a linguist is not mainly learning languages as such. I work with the technical description of languages—how they are put together, whether they use systems of prefixes or suffixes, what families they belong to, and that sort of thing. We get into a language by recognizing its family, then analyzing its structure. Personally, I have a working knowledge of only a few languages besides English—Spanish, French, German, Portugese, Greek, Latin, and Hebrew. That's not many, as languages go."

He cocked his head on one side, and for a moment gazed reflectively out the window at the clear January afternoon, its skies as crisply blue as his eyes. "You know, some people urge us to share 'our' religion. Others say that we shouldn't force 'our' religion on others. The trouble is the word 'our.' *Our* religion? Where do we get it? Christ made himself known to a handful of people, and the command to go and preach to all nations is very practical, because Christianity by its nature cannot be contained. It is a transforming faith, let loose in the world. It belongs to that community of Otomi Indians just as much as it does to us, and they take it more seriously than many of us do, and they are showing the Christian faith to others. They are missionaries, you see."

· 4 ·

Forest Boy—Knight of Faith

"Our flight time from Benin to Enugu will be approximately one hour," the Nigerian stewardess said crisply. "We will be flying below the clouds." The poet fastened his seat belt. The DC-3 growled down the runway and bounced off, lifting until it climbed over the dense forest palms.

In Enugu he would interview Sir Francis Ibiam, a boy from the inland bush who had become Governor of Eastern Nigeria. He was fashioning modern Africa out of the past, a past that actually went back to the cultures and kingdoms and arts that had once flourished, like the Norse and other tribal cultures of northern Europe. All had died out, though portions of the European cultures had been revived and used in Christian civilization. From this civilization, Africa had been colonized commercially and politically. But its peoples and past cultures had not been transformed by Christianity, as had the pagan cultures of

Europe. So now, the poet wondered, what did the mission of a Sir Francis do?

They were flying very low, beneath a rumple of gray clouds that dropped no rain. It was the dry season. The poet looked down at the dense, green vegetation of tropical rain forest. They were so low he could see the coconuts on some of the palms, and recognize avocado and banana trees. He imagined himself down there, on a narrow dirt train that he saw angling through the green palms. Have an avocada or banana? Prefer a papaya? In ages past, foodgathering had been little challenge, but now many of the forests had been reserved. Also, in large areas one couldn't plow and raise crops. The soil was not good; just a thin skin of topsoil over poor laterite. Plowed soil would yield one poor crop, and wash out at the first rain. What with this, and wild game, there hadn't been the need or opportunity to develop advanced agricultural economics.

Then the poet remembered standing a few days before at the forest's edge. He felt the hot, dank darkness of it. A quietness had come upon him, and the forest had seemed to tick with hidden life. He had passed a dead bird, and passed it again an hour later, and seen a skeleton. Above it, the leaves and stems of plants still grew, too incredibly huge, green, and bulging. There were flies, carrying diseases, and there were parasites in the streams, up and down the length of Africa.

The wet ground of dead leaves had squeaked beneath his feet. Something moved softly in a tree, but he couldn't see it. There were sounds, and things lived and moved unseen, among the bulging leaves. He let his mind run. . . .

Tic-tic, tic-tic-tic, koo-koo-ka-dee-koo. Gldrr. The sound came from the middle of those leaves. There was something there. Perhaps there was a tree spirit. Yes, and a ground spirit made the trees grow. Perhaps there were water spirits in the dark streams.

Look, he came home like that from the stream, with his tongue swollen and his eyes bulging. It must be a bad water spirit. You think a water spirit? He came from the water, and it was in him. What can we do? Put him near the fire, and perhaps the smoke will drive out the water spirit. Yes, but he is still choking—see? And what is that sound, high in the trees? It is the wind. But listen, the wind is talking. It is the wind spirit. Perhaps it will drive out the bad water spirit, the way the wind drives the water on the lake. Yes, ask the wind spirit. Beseech the wind spirit: boom, boom-boom. . . .

As the poet flew forward into modern Africa, his imagination had drifted back into the primitive past, an elemental past that lay buried even in his own mind, and that seemed to wake and stir as he meditated on the warm, ticking darkness of the forest. Life and death were so redundant there, swiftly alternating and juxtaposed, in a bulging and dying profusion that wasn't geared to the long rhythm of the temperate nature cycle: the rhythm of the nature religions with which the world's first civilizations rose. Now, Africa was called to a civilized development beyond nature religions.

Beneath the plane now, the jungle was dropping away and the land was rising. The country was becoming more open, with elephant grass and clumps of woods. They were coming over the high country. The rain forest was not the norm. It grew in a few coastal regions, and along the big rivers, which was why European explorers had seen so much of it. But most of Africa was high grassland, where tribes had followed the wild herds. Their people had grown tall and healthy. Now industry was coming, suitable farming methods were needed, and more modern medicine was required.

All these could be valuable expressions of the Christian mission. But there was also a need more basic than these, or the adapting of forest or grassland ways to modern life. Christianity had *transformed* the older cultures of Europe. Wouldn't there be a *transforming* nub in the mission of Sir Francis?

"Please fasten your seat belts," the stewardess said. "We are landing in Enugu."

In an hour, they had jumped from Benin to Enugu. A few generations ago, this was more than a long and hot distance to go on foot. It meant the distance between different peoples, different languages, and different ways, one adapted to grasslands and the other to forest. Modern transport and communications made a big difference. Yet communication by drum or runner had been fairly quick, when desired. Still something was lacking. Some sort of basic, concrete transformation was needed.

A few minutes later, as the poet walked from the plane to the small airport building, his name was called by a slender, erect young African officer, about six feet tall, dressed in a natty khaki uniform. He introduced himself as the aide-de-camp to Sir Francis, the governor. He was to take the poet to the State House, which served Sir Francis and Lady Ibiam as both a residence and place of official business. The poet, who had been expecting to make his own way into Enugu, and stay at its one inn, was delighted.

The Governor's car was a dark gray Chevrolet sedan, with the official crest carried on plates on the front and rear bumpers. The poet rode in back with the aide-de-camp—the A.D.C., as he was called—while an African chauffeur drove. They went along a tarred road, dusty at the sides, and hemmed by the dense elephant grass, which grew taller than a man. Men in shorts with open shirts, and shoeless, walked or bicycled along the sides. The road led uphill, and within a few minutes they were swinging into the gravel drive of the State House, which stood atop a ridge.

It was about a hundred yards long and two spacious stories high. The walls were glass, but were protected from the sun by exterior columns, narrow and deep, with baffles added near the top. From the main house, a covered walkway spanned cleanly across the end of the drive, past a rounded flower bed where huge, orange-red lilies grew, and to a smaller, two-story building of the same design—"where His Excellency works," the A.D.C. said. It struck the poet as a beautiful instance of contemporary design adapted to Africa, and it seemed an incredible piece of luxury to come upon suddenly, after driving through the elephant grass among the barefoot walkers and bicyclers.

They passed a sentry box, with the uniformed sentry saluting. They passed some comfortable outbuildings, looking like small ranch houses in an American suburb. The staff lived in these. The car swept up to the wide, shaded glass doors of the State House. The house staff was on hand, uniformed in white.

Sir Francis and Lady Ibiam came forward simply, in modest dress. They shook hands quietly and greeted him cordially. Sir Francis was a man of moderate stature, with a keen glance and gentle voice. His graying hair grew close to his head and made a clear contrast to his dark brown complexion. He wore a lightweight suit in dark brown, while Lady Ibiam wore a neat, dark dress with a subdued floral design.

Then the A.D.C. showed the poet to his room in the spacious guest quarters on the second story. There was an air conditioner, though the poet didn't turn it on, because only the bedrooms were air-conditioned, and he didn't want to step from coldness into a steam-bath heat. Luncheon would be served in half an hour. The poet decided that a jacket and a tie would be in order. The A.D.C. left.

The poet was grateful to Sir Francis for his unasked and gracious hospitality. Yet he flung his bags around the room, yanked out the black summer suit he had brought for his interviews with Sir Francis, found some cold water in the spacious bathroom with which to wash his face, and stamped up and down the room . . . huge glass house . . . guards . . . white uniforms . . . suits and ties, and he wanted desperately to strip to his shorts and go swimming in the State House pool, and sit under the shady trees in a breeze. He flung himself on the bed. The whole thing was so different from the informality that he knew, the hurly-burly of the big city's streets, the coffee shop where life was casual and yet intense, and the apartment where he lived a relaxed life with his wife. But this was ridiculous. . . .

Suddenly, a phrase crossed his mind, "cultural shock." He was suffering from this, he realized. His very sensitivity probably made him more open to it than others. But suits and ties? He was sweating from every pore. The heat was all around him, like an invisible steam towel. It wasn't the mean temperature; he had felt hotter in New York and had been insulted when Britishers called it torrid. But *this* was torrid. It was temperature and humidity, and something more . . . a sort of laziness, a lazy timelessness, that made him want to take off most of his clothes and just let life flow along, with as little effort as possible. He pulled himself together, put on a white summer shirt, black suit, and red tie, and went to lunch. He would find out how a disciple of the Christ, who had lived so simply, could possible be exercising a mission here.

The meal was signaled by a gong. It was served in the smaller dining room. The large rooms were only for formal state occasions. The Governor bowed quietly and simply, his black and graying hair above the white table linen, and said grace. Then, the conversation proceeded in English. Besides the poet, Sir Francis and Lady Ibiam were entertaining the director and heir of a big French industrial firm and his two assistants. Their firm was the oldest rubber concern in France. They were in Nigeria to develop a rubber plantation and tire factory. This was part of Sir Francis' work, to foster industrial development. His post was appointive and nonpartisan, like that of a monarch, though he was more involved in affairs than a monarch.

The meal was served by houseboys in white uniforms. It started with tomato soup, which was followed by fish in patty shells. The talk was leisurely, dealing with Nigerian development. More roads were being tarred every day. The fish was followed by well-done beef, with carrots, green beans, and boiled skinless potatoes. On the cement porch outside, two lizards about eight inches long, black with flaming streamers of orange, were trekking along. The poet questioned Sir Francis politely about Nigerian development and the need for hard work.

"Yes," he replied. "We're concentrating on industry and farming. The young men need to learn that when they become educated, it is honorable and responsible to go back to the farm. We're starting village farming communities. The land is pooled, then owned and occupied by the participating villagers. We need agricultural experts to help us. We need to develop educated Nigerians who will work on the farm. This is difficult."

One of the houseboys began clearing the main course. It was replaced by ice cream topped by a sugary fluff and canned peaches, and finally by cheese. Everything on the table was grown and made in Africa, Lady Ibiam said, except the canned peaches. She said it in a way that had a bit of a humorous twist. In New York, the poet had heard that Lady Ibiam "had quite a sense of humor." Her sense of humor was subtle, a thing of bright eyes and calm comments.

After lunch, they sat for half an hour in the adjoining lounge, a room about twenty by thirty feet. Two of its walls were shaded windows, and the other two were paneled. The furniture was a medium brown in color, made of hardwood, and superbly designed in a simple, contemporary manner. It reminded the poet of some of the finest examples of American colonial furniture that he had seen in the Metropolitan Museum of Art. He came from a long tradition of artists and craftsmen, and his inbred and trained sense of artistry told him that he was looking at some of the best furniture ever designed and crafted. The writing desk with its high back was an especially fine piece. In response to his compliments, Sir Francis said, "It was designed in Sweden, but made in Nigeria, with Nigerian wood."

Soon, everyone retired for the afternoon nap. The poet took off his jacket and shirt and lay on the bed. It didn't seem so very hot. The State House surroundings were fancy, he reflected, but the meal and formalities had been simple enough. There was nothing lush or exotic. He drifted quickly into a torpid sleep, and woke forty-five minutes later on a pillow wet with perspiration. For the next half hour, he dozed fitfully. Then there was a knock on the door. He put on his shirt and opened it.

A houseboy entered with a tray of tea, breads, and cookies. Nigeria certainly had been a British colony. "Thank you, though I'm really not hungry," the poet said.

"I leave it here." The houseboy set the tray on a table next to one of the armchairs.

"Thank you." This was the rhythm of the State House. It was time for tea, and tea was served. One rose early, worked through the morning, had lunch, took a nap, had tea, and put in several more hours of work. So the day was ordered. However lazy and casual he felt, he could not resist the rhythm of this order. The hot tea tasted good, despite the humid heat around him. He tried one of the breads, enjoyed it, and had another. Half an hour later, the houseboy picked up a completely empty tray from the room of the unhungry poet.

The poet interviewed Sir Francis in his office, talking with him across his polished desk. Once again, as when he had arrived, there was the feeling of subtle shock. He sensed that it came from the contrast, the setting of a monarch in which this man moved with simple dignity. The poet had trouble with his tape recorder, and apologized. "That's quite all right," Sir Francis said. His eyes and mind seemed to be elsewhere, his whole attitude saying, "It's quite all right, take your time," as the poet struggled, then pushed the machine aside and took notes.

Responding to questions, Sir Francis told about his past. "I was born in Unwana, in 1906. It's about a hundred miles east of here. You will go there tomorrow, if you wish. I have arranged for you to have the car, my A.D.C., and a chauffeur and boy for the day." Once more the poet was impressed with the simple graciousness of the man who, forgoing the lavish drinking and eating habits of many men in similar positions, unhesitatingly put his own car, his A.D.C., and two servants at the complete disposal of the poet. Christian dignity and kindness were being given concrete expression by this man in these surroundings.

"You should leave at five," Sir Francis was saying, "or six at the latest. . . . "

The next day, the poet took his notes and memories of the interview, and recalled them during the trip to Sir Francis' hometown.

The sun was almost up. They were barreling along the narrow road. He was heading into the back country, the poet reflected, and backward in time. By doing this and coming forward again, he might discern the transforming nub of Sir Francis' mission. Men were walking and bicycling to work along the road. Their postures were always superbly erect. And no wonder; they carried things on their heads.

Here was a whole family carrying things. On his head the man was bearing a stack of wood, its stout poles six feet long. One of the older boys also walked with a load of wood. The woman, wearing only a skirt, was carrying a bushel-sized basket of African yams, which looked like irregular tan footballs. The younger children were bearing smaller baskets of yams. They all walked in long and easy strides in the red roadside dust beside the elephant grass.

"My father cultivated yams, like everyone else in his time," Sir Francis had said. "They are still a staple. But we are trying to diversify agriculture and get more heavy industry. I'm helping in these ways." His Excellency the Governor was "helping," the poet reflected, musing on the man's modesty.

They came to a railroad crossing, and here amid the trees and grass was a big plant and sign: Nigersteel Company Ltd. It was a rolling mill. Now here were cattle being driven by the roadside. They were rangy, with long horns, and some were colored black, some brown. For this little time, before sunrise, there was a freshness in the air.

"Our beef comes from northern Nigeria," he remembered Sir Francis saying. "The cattle are raised there, then shipped and driven to market."

The roadside of red clay earth was spinning past. Now people were carrying baskets of sand on their heads. The sand is for making cement, for those who can afford it. Most people use wattle. There is a river ahead—Ekulu River—there, they are digging the sand along the wide banks. The sun is up now, coming red over the palms. It is getting warmer.

Here is a whole covey of women, wearing bright flowery skirts. They are carrying big baskets of yams. And here is another covey of women, carrying baskets of longer, thinner roots—cassava. Here is a field where yams are raised, growing in red earth mounds about three feet high. Ahead and coming now is a cassava field. The mounds are smaller and the plants look like small, delicate sumac bushes. Here are more women and some men, carrying mostly oranges. They are also coming from among the trees and elephant grass, wending out of narrow trails. Quite a few are coming out of this village, carrying things on their heads. Some of the baskets hold palm nuts. The village houses are one-story high, about ten by twenty feet. The roofs are thatched waterproof with woven palm leaves, and the walls are made with wattle—woven sticks heavily plastered with clay-like mud that was baked dry by the sun.

Ahead there come more houses, thatched roofs but no walls. The people are gathering here, taking their baskets from their heads, bending with limber arms, spreading out their oranges and yams and bananas and palm nuts and jars of palm oil and baskets of cassava. The unwalled houses serve as market stalls. The people from miles around gather here every few days, trading, buying, selling.

"My father sold yams," Sir Francis had said. "He traded in palm oil and palm nuts. He carried them on his head to market. He died when my brother and I were very small, and my mother remarried."

The sun was higher, and the humid air was growing warmer. The poet asked the A.D.C. if wild animals provided much food anymore. "No, they have mostly all been shot. But sometimes people still shoot an antelope or a grass cutter." From his description, a grass cutter sounded like a very large guinea pig. The poet was beginning to feel lazy again. Apparently, one needed a lot of sleep in this climate.

The car was slowing. They were coming to a larger town. There was a sign:

GO SLOW

THROUGH

ABAKALIKI

Here were the low, solid buildings of a government college and secondary school. "They have a fine cricket team." Here were some larger houses made of cement, as well as the wattle houses. They turned right. Beside the road stood a few stores, cement or wattle with little signs, and there was a shed with a rice mill buzzing away, run by a donkey engine. Along the road men were pushing big handcarts of rice, carts big enough to require a tractor or a team of mules. Beyond, he saw the marshes where the rice grew.

MEN FOR OTHERS

"We are building up rice as an industry." Sir Francis had said. His manner was matter-of-fact, and cautiously pleased. "We are milling our own rice now. This is an advance. But we need more machines, and people with your American know-how. This is something you have and can share."

The Nigerian men were struggling up the slight incline, pushing the heavy carts of rice. Now the road became dusty. The tar was gone. They entered a construction zone, where a few small road machines were making slow progress. Then there were a few more towns:

GO SLOW

THROUGH

EZIKWO

Sir Francis' hometown of Unwana lay on a ridge, high over the broad and meandering Cross River. The town had ten thousand people, the Governor had said. But only a few dozen people and houses could be seen. Some houses were cement, but most were made of wattle. The trees had mostly not been cut down. The houses extended into wooded areas, one family compound after another, and many were unseen. It was a city, in harmony with nature: something that Africa could teach New York, the poet reflected, musing on how pleasant and healthy his city would be if the smog were cut, people walked and bicycled more, the streets were lined with big trees, and the buildings grown with evergreen and flowering vines.

As they walked in the forest city, small chickens scattered before them. They typically ran loose in Africa. Nobody stole them, or concentrated on raising them. They laid eggs here and there, and provided meat for wedding feasts, and everyone had enough food to eat. The economy of the tribal towns made a simple use of common abundance.

They came to a gateway, went through, and walked now in an extensive section of attached wattle houses. They were partly shaded by palms. It was dusty, with no breeze, and the air was close. Here is where St. Francis had been born and reared until he was ten.

"My father opened a new section of the town with his compound," he had said. "The man has a house for himself, and the women each have a house. The children live with their mothers until they are about ten. Then the boys go to live with their fathers, and the girls continue with their mothers." Now here were the houses, some made of mud-and-stick rooms added to rooms, and thatched waterproof with woven palm. Others were of sturdier, more permanent materials.

Children darted in little alleys among the brown houses and peered at the visitors. Women looked at them from doorways, or greeted them a bit shyly as they passed. Often they wore nothing but skirts. Their bare chests were accepted naturally here, because breasts are for feeding children, not for making a fuss about. Perhaps Sir Francis' hometown was more adult than modern America in this respect.

The A.D.C. led the way to a couple of houses connected by a thatched porch. Here a thin, aged woman with wrinkled skin was sitting in the sun, slowly mashing some yellow meal with a little pestle in a wooden bowl. She was introduced, and looked up slowly toward the

American poet, her wrinkled face gnome-like. He saw from her milky eyes that she was completely blind. This was the reality behind a cold statistic, showing too few doctors in Africa. She spoke in the Ibo tongue, and one of the nearby men translated:

"She gives you greetings, and says she is very glad you could come."

"Tell her," the poet said slowly, "that I am glad to be here, and appreciate the hospitality."

The reply pleased her; she smiled broadly. The poet passed on with the little group of men. They walked on broad paths through the compound. Narrow alleys angled off from these. The place was the size of a village now, but had been started by Sir Francis' father.

"He and my mother were not church people," Sir Francis had said. "But they believed in God. My father had a shrine to Chi-neke, which means 'God-who-created.'" So God had created, and life simply went on. Compounds were extended, or perhaps fell into disuse. The poet was not struck by changes in architecture or monuments to the past. The days went by and both life and death flowed steadily on.

In a wedge of shade beside a house, three boys were sitting cross-legged in the dust. They were weaving a net onto a hoop stick. "We used to trap birds," the Governor had said. "Sometimes we went fishing in the river. We caught only little fish."

When they stepped from the compound, a few men and children stood by the car. The word had gone around: the Governor's car was in town. The State House was felt. There was not a crowd, in the Western sense. The watchers were scattered. There were several by a tree and some by another. Others were simply walking by, seeming casual, but observing. People emerged quietly from a dozen paths or disappeared into them. More people had materialized in the path behind them. The poet saw only a few at a time. But he knew he was among thousands.

An educated young man, who had evidently served Sir Francis, stopped to chat for a minute with the A.D.C. He gave an impromptu lesson in Africa's traditional system of social security. A relative had died, he was explaining, and plans were being made to care for the women and children. It was as simple as that. The larger family was responsible for the dependents. There was not a single person in a town like this who lacked a home or was destitute by African standards. There were no beggars. There were no homeless children.

Now they drove a short distance to the school. Its buildings were made in the same ranch style, but were longer, with higher roofs, and the walls didn't go all the way to the ceiling. The school lay on the side of the ridge. Like most of Africa's schools, it had been started by the church —Scottish Presbyterian Church, in this case.

Atop the hill, children about six years of age waited in a long, talkative, but quite orderly line. From this hill crest, the poet could see the broad and gently winding Cross River, far below in the sun. The children were waiting to register for school. But there were not enough rooms or teachers for all. In their day, Sir Francis and his brother Samuel had been among those who had attended school, but this had been at a time when fewer children were interested in doing so.

"When we were small boys," Sir Francis had said, "we believed in juju. We thought that some people had juju in them, and could give it to you"—he had made a flicking gesture with his fingers—"and this would make you sick. Or we thought a person had juju, and couldn't be beaten in a fight. We believed that if a person walked into darkness, he would disappear."

From down the hill, in an auditorium-type room, there came the high, melodious voices of African children learning a hymn to the God of light, "He who fed the mul-ti-tude. . . . " the voices sang. The school went through the primary grades. Its principal and teachers were all Nigerians.

"When boys came of age," the Governor had related, "the town was closed to women, and the men conducted initiation ceremonies. The boys ran a beating gauntlet. But I didn't do this. My brother was at Hope-Waddell— started by Scottish missionaries—and my uncle had become educated, and the Christian influence of the schools was taking away my superstition. I went down the river to Hope-Waddell, too. I was about ten then. My best subject was English, and my favorite books when I learned to read were Lamb's *Tales from Shakespeare* and Andersen's *Fairy Tales*."

The poet looked down the steep ridge to the river below. Some birds resembling pelicans, black with big yellow bills, were flying casually along the river or roosting in eucalyptus trees. His eyes began to trace the distance, along the river to where it disappeared into the hazy horizon. It must be about a hundred miles, down from this country to the school at Calabar near the coast.

There missionaries, refusing to be discouraged, had contended with rituals of fear and murder, resolutely establishing the school.

"Christianity is the real antidote to superstition and its fears," Sir Francis had stated quietly. "I found this release from fears at the school, and became a Christian before long. There were two hundred boarding students, from all over Nigeria, and we had many day students. We competed keenly in everything. You couldn't be a mama's boy there. You became strong and self-reliant. The school built stamina into me.

"I remember our course in moral instruction. We would deal with a subject such as honesty, then take examples and discuss them. We also learned to be punctual, and the habit has stayed with me to this day.

"From Hope-Waddell," he continued, "I went to college in Lagos, then to St. Andrews' University in Scotland, and through medical school. My brother was working as a language translator by then, and he paid for my schooling. He died before I finished school but left enough money for me to finish. I became a doctor, and returned to Nigeria as a medical missionary. I found that as a missionary I would never have the money to give my children an advanced education—and I wanted them to excel me. My contemporaries were earning four or five times as much as I earned. I knew I could have done the same.

"But I never hungered to be in their position. I had chosen my work and was happy in it." He recalled how he had gone to Abiriba, in Eastern Nigeria, and singlehandedly had started a hospital under the auspices of the

Church of Scotland Mission (now the Presbyterian Church of Nigeria). Some of the village men had helped him clear the land. The young doctor had worked from dawn to dark. At night he had studied the latest medical journals that he could get his hands on, with his wiry figure bending over the pages by the light of a kerosene lamp.

In 1937, the hospital had an operating room, four staff houses, a doctor's house, and a ward for thirty-two patients, divided into male and female sections. Each sick person was cared for by some member of his family. The system of family and group security remained intact, but the health and medical attitudes of the area were being transformed.

He married in 1939. His wife, a Lagos girl, had also been to school in the United Kingdom, and was a nurse. They had their three children in the 1940's. There were two girls, Alu and Tolulope, and a boy named Aka. Dr. Ibiam continued to build up the hospital work, and was knighted in 1951 for his achievements. Then he was drawn into politics, first at the regional level, and became a solid champion of Nigerian independence. He also became a leader in Nigerian Christian work.

The poet walked down the slope, through the open schoolyard where the children were still rehearsing the song: "He who fed the mul-ti-tude. . . . " He walked with the A.D.C. and a couple of townsmen. The sun was hot overhead, and the air moist; flop under a tree, the climate seemed to say. It must have taken sustained stamina for a boy from an inland town in this climate to blaze a trail of faith and works.

At the end of the school area, a woman was sitting beneath a tree nursing a child, while a younger woman sat calmly by. As they passed, the nursing woman screamed and screeched incoherently at them.

"She's mad!" the A.D.C. exclaimed.

"Yes," a townsman replied simply.

"But she's nursing a child!" His military figure moved erectly, and his voice was shocked.

"Yes," the townsman replied again. "She nurses." She had a place. The big family of the village cared for its insane. She even had a legitimate function: "She nurses." It was something she could do.

The visiting party retired to a comfortable house for a hot lunch and cold drink. A little later, by the main road of the town, they stopped for a moment by a small, white tomb by the roadside. The headstone read:

Unfading and Loving Memory of
Alu Owora
Departed this Life 15 September, 1949
to be
"for ever with the Lord"

Sir Francis' mother was buried here. By the common roadside, her son His Excellency had made the tomb a simple and dignified statement of faith for all to see. It was startling: because here for the first time, there was a moment that stated a definite past and implied a definite future—that showed a real sense of *history*, as it was understood by the progressive mind. And the progressive sense of history, the poet reflected, could be traced through Christianity and back deeply into Judaism. So Sir Francis has a mission in history. This is near the nub of the thing.

They climbed into the car. The chauffeur released the brake, the Governor's hometown of Unwana fell behind, and soon they were barreling along, the roadside grass, trees, and wattle houses spinning past. They were hurtling forward in time now, back toward the State House. The poet looked up his notes on the Governor's political career.

1946: elected to Legislative Council in Lagos. 1949: elected to Executive Council, one of four Nigerians. 1953: left politics voluntarily. He left when power and reward were coming, and coming more easily each year. So these couldn't have been his motives. On his mind's eye, the poet saw Sir Francis leaning across his polished desk, his intent face framed by the close thatch of graying hair as he explained:

"We were not independent at the time. We had to fight Britain to win back our historic independence. This was the first task. But political parties had developed, and I didn't think we were ready for these. I didn't want to contribute to factionalism when I felt that the major task at that time was winning back our independence from Britain.

"So I went back to the medical mission, and worked at the hospital at Uburu for about five years. Then I was asked to take charge of Hope-Waddell Training Institute." He was its first Nigerian principal. During this period he emerged as a leading African churchman, presiding over the first All-Africa Church Conference in 1958. He became known internationally and was asked to consultations in Asia and America. When Nigeria became independent, he was appointed Governor of the big eastern region, and installed on December 15, 1960. From his map, the poet knew that Nigeria had the largest population of any African nation—about 40 million—and was divided into three sizable regions. They were semiautonomous and differed somewhat from each other, like the major states in the early days of the American republic.

"The Governorship was completely unexpected," Sir Francis had said. "I was happy in medicine and educational work."

This was probably one reason he had been chosen. He sought no advantage himself. So now he could function like the frame of a car, holding things together and allowing progress while one political engine or another was tried. All this was part of his mission. Fostering industry and agriculture was part of his mission. Eastern Nigeria was establishing farm settlements and trade schools, expanding the number of science teachers via special inducements, and making every effort to attract industrial development.

But technology doesn't form the center and goal of human striving, the poet realized.

They had stopped in Abakaliki for minor repairs. The rice mill buzzed next to the small repair shop. The poet walked down the road, and stood looking at one of the ant cities. The ants had transformed acres of ground with their technology. Many of the yellow-brown mounds and pillars stood as tall as a man, and some taller. They were full of tunnels and ramparts. Man, on his scale, had not matched the achievement with the pyramids, because the pyramids were simply tombs. The ant buildings provided working quarters and housing. Men hadn't matched the achievement on their scale until they built the modern skyscraper cities.

The ants began doing this in miniature a million years ago. The poet stood in the humid bronze of the African sun, looking at the ant city with its towers and ramparts and ticking busyness, and saw the dead end of technology. It was a dangerous fascination, to which the ants had succumbed. Technology and life had become one, and the ants' development had ceased nearly a million years ago. He walked soberly back to Abakaliki, musing on the fate of a creature that had become the servant of its own technology, instead of vice-versa.

The State House car had drawn a moderate crowd. The people weren't closely clustered. They observed from the doors of a few shops, and from yards, or strolled past. The owner of the repair shop had arrived in a polished green Volkswagon. Once again, it was evident that the influence of Sir Francis was felt. The poet walked into one of the shops. Here was African pottery, Nigerian Star lager beer, and imported canned goods. And there were books—*books*, here in this bush town where the silence seemed broken only by the buzzing little mill. The racks offered such selections as Stephen Neil's *Anglicanism,* D. H. Lawrence's *Sons and Lovers, The Koran,* and *Winnie-the-Pooh.*

The rice mill helped people have the time and money to buy and read the books. That was the proper way with technology. The content of Sir Francis' political mission was civilization, moving into history from a Christian base. The poet remembered the words of an inner-city missionary in New York: "Politics are evangelism. They work to bring alive the things that make and keep people human." And Sir Francis in his inaugural address had said, "Not by power nor by might, but by my spirit, saith the Lord of hosts." He had meant it. The concrete, transforming nub of Sir Francis' mission was beginning to emerge.

That evening, in the briefly cooler time before darkness, Sir Francis invited the poet to stroll in the new garden off the end of the State House. The flower beds were laid in broad, orderly strips, and gravel was going down on the paths. At the end of the garden there stood a tree like a cottonwood, where a flock of crimson birds with black wings was beginning to roost. His Excellency talked and listened in his quiet way, turning thoughts over in his mind. Yet he could become suddenly sharp and probing.

"We can see ten miles from here," he remarked. "Our pottery works and furniture factory are down there, over the ridge," and he gestured. "The main part of Enugu is beyond." He was a man who was helping to father a country. Each day from his desk, he extended some of the content of civilization.

"Many roads have been tarred since independence. Why couldn't the British have done it?" And his voice turned a bit sharp. The sun was low now, a dull orange disk that hung over the hills. Sir Francis pointed out some of the new garden plants, of the kind that grow well in the American south. The poet asked for his views on race relations in the United States and those in South Africa.

"It's inhuman, uncivilized." He stopped in the path and looked at the poet. His delicately lined face seemed wise and curious at the same time, and his eyes were brightly quizzical. "I saw pictures of some young men in your country, jeering at a girl because of her color. Why do people do this? What makes them act that way?" His voice was impatient.

The poet thought of his meditation on the jungle, and replied: "It seems to be a reversion to savagery."

"We were the ones called savages," he replied, "as though we were a lower form of man." He gestured impatiently. "I cannot understand what makes people think like this." The voice was that of a man too steeped in his faith and civilized ways to imagine the motives of racists.

They continued their quiet walk in the garden. Suddenly, the quiet was split by a bugle at the State House gate: taps were sounding. It was growing quickly darker. Lights were already coming on in Enugu, and would be doing the same in Abakaliki. The countryside had begun living to a different drum, a rhythm and order that radiated from the State House.

In a flash, there emerged the nub of the Governor's political mission: *time*. Sir Francis was transforming *time*. In his moody imaginings prompted by the jungle, and again in Unwana, the poet had felt primitive time: Life went around and around, with the moon, or with the alternating wet and dry periods. But Sir Francis from his position in the State House was transforming primitive time into history.

Time and events no longer flowed forward without historic purpose, the same today as yesterday. Time and events were ordered, moving toward goals, driving forward with historic and unfolding purpose. This was a gift from the Judaic-Christian understanding of God as *Lord of history*, revealing himself and unfolding his purposes. With him, time was historic and ongoing. The State House was a major agency for transforming primitive time, giving new order and new events and ongoing purpose. This was the transforming nub of Sir Francis' politican mission.

The twilight was deepening around them. From the darkness overhead there came an eerie cry, "wik-wik, wik-wik-wik." The poet studied the firm, oval planes of the Governor's delicately lined face, and reflected on a statement by the Asian theologian D. T. Niles: "One thing a missionary does is to bear witness to the integrity of the secular. He goes to say that a tree is a tree, not the home of spirits, and a bird is a bird. . . ." And from overhead again came the cry, "wik-wik, wik-wik-wik."

"One of our nighthawks," Sir Francis said. He and the poet walked in darkness now, but did not disappear. Ahead of them, the lights of the State House were coming on, beaconing the sultry night, and lesser lights had gone on across the hills and valleys. Sir Francis was helping father history itself. With the mind of his faith, using the ceremony, order, and powers of the State House, Sir Francis was acting to transform time. He was turning time into history, and putting into it the content of civilization.

They walked together into the bright, beaconing State House. Sir Francis remarked: "I don't accept Christianity as an easy way. It is difficult to be faithful, to be honest, to be true, and to lead a life that many people don't ascribe to. Yet I find that if you tread that way, you are a happy man, and you are strong, and you are in a position to give other people help."

On the way to dinner, they passed a superb ebony carving of a wild animal, used as a book end for the Bible, Shakespeare, and Aristotle. At dinner, they bowed over the white linen cloth as the Governor said grace. His mission here was to be preeminently a civilized man who lived and radiated the history and ethics of his faith.

· 5 ·

Ambassador of Brotherhood

LEANING back in his swivel chair in a polished office of
the Interchurch Center was a squarely-built man who
had fought his way from the ramshackle slums of Knoxville to his present position as vice-president of the Peace
Corps and informal advisor to the American mission at the
United Nations. The man was James H. Robinson, the
founder and chief of Operation Crossroads-Africa, which
had provided inspiration and a model for the Peace Corps.

Jim swiveled around in the chair, gazed out a lofty
window across the Hudson River, and with his free arm
reached across his graying, closely cropped hair to scratch
his ear at the telephone receiver. The call was from one
of the more than 1,500 college age applicants for the interfaith, interracial summer work camps run by Crossroads
in Africa. Jim had interrupted his interview to take the
call, as available to this college student as he was to the
American Ambassador at the United Nations.

"No, Virginia," he was saying, "no, don't apologize for calling. If you do, then I'll say I'm sorry you called. So you have to take it back. So long." With a grin he hung up.

He was tired from a night of jet travel. His square shoulders sagged slightly in his brown suit. As he looked at the poet, his eyes closed to sleepy slits, yet brimmed with humor. There was a grin on his almost round face. He wore a small, neat moustache, like a gray-black line sketched on the upper lip of his brown face. Jim leaned forward at the desk, folding his hands and speaking forcefully:

"My whole point of view has been to make a rapid change of attitude and strategy in the United States about our relation to the awakening nations of Africa. Things happen so fast in Africa today that a week is a long time, and we don't have a chance to fiddle around." He paused, and his face took on a suggestion of irony. "I guess I'm kind of a maverick, wishing things could move faster—much faster—and much more creatively. And I like to knock a bung out of things, and let the oil of life pour a good deal more freely."

He smiled wryly, then more warmly. His eyes were intensely expressive. They had narrowed to slits again, and crinkled with amusement at the corners. The poet tossed out a question about blatant racial bigotry, and watched Jim's eyes.

They opened wide, hardening with a deep anger that was belied by his calm voice as he discussed and denounced the sin of bigotry. "Do I not hate them that hate thee, O Lord?" the poet remembered from Psalm 139. "I hate them with perfect hatred. . . ." the psalmist continued, and the poet heard Jim saying: "You and I can hate the sin, but we love the sinner." This was the "perfect hatred" that the psalmist hadn't described, and the poet mentally underscored Jim's "you and I," and "we"; he as a white man was being included.

Now Jim's face was relaxing, a smile coming to the corners of his mouth. Racial bigotry seemed a tangible thing, sitting right there on the desk. Jim had taken its measure, and his eyes fanned slowly open and shut, like those of a Cheshire cat meditating on the Absolute Mouse. Now he stalked the tough mouse of bigotry, saying in effect: Fight the good fight for brotherhood, forge cooperation—"if we would only get to know each other better, honestly know each other as human beings, as children of God. . . ."

Had Jim learned to look at himself in this way? He began to tell his story, which started with his birth in "the Bottoms" of Knoxville in 1907.

The first thing from which he "knocked a bung," Jim acknowledged, was "out of my attitude about myself." He added: "I grew up in the South, where I had learned to accept the attitude that as a Negro there was nothing I could do—no contribution I could make—and like so many other people in my neighborhood and my own family, I began to succumb to this. Then I came to the place where I began to know that wasn't right, and I felt I had some destiny, and so I had to break with my family to get an education. This meant living on beans and bread for two winters and having no place to sleep and being laughed at—my own family thought it was a crazy idea. . . ." His voice dwindled reflectively as he recalled these early years.

In "the Bottoms," where he spent his early boyhood,

"our homes were hardly more than rickety shacks, clustered on stilts like Daddy Long Legs along the slimy bank of putrid and evil-smelling Cripple Creek. Hemmed in by the muddy creek bank on one side, by tobacco warehouses and a foundry on another, and by slaughter pens on a third, it was a world set apart and excluded. When the wind blew in our direction the combined stench of outhouses and slaughter pens was unbearable." The water supply for the community came from a single spigot, "rising out of the yellowish ooze of mud at a crazy angle." In summer, the section was airless and dry. In winter, the creek would sometimes flood, the foul waters rumbling beneath the stilted shacks. Jim and his older brother remembered, fearfully, the biblical story of the flood. There were frequent cases of smallpox, typhoid fever, and tuberculosis. He was hungry most of the time, he indicated, and the poet recalled that the gnawing desire for food pervaded even the imagery in the early pages of his autobiography, *Road without Turning:* The mud was "hardened cake," the sun would "bake" the ground, the spigot water was "good tasting."

His father, Jim said, was a zealous member of the flamboyant "Sanctified Church." His fierce thanksgivings before Sunday dinner, when there was one, would frequently last so long that the food was cold. His mother, a devout believer in quiet ways, would often harangue his father about the time and money he spent at the "Sanctified Church." Later, when she was buried—it was two days after Christmas—the "Sanctified" preacher predicted for her the fires of Hell, prancing and clapping his hands as he vividly depicted her endless torment. She would be punished because she was "unsanctified." Jim was sickened and shaken by the incident.

He recalled that his mother had frequently been sick, battling with her weakness as she took in washing to earn some extra money. Sometimes, his father would come home from work in the freight yards to find her weakly contending with a tub of wash. Then he would pick her up bodily, tuck her into bed, roll up his sleeves, and finish the wash himself. Jim also described times when the whole community was flooded, he and his brother were nearly sick with hunger—and his father, unable to find work, would stand at the broken windows, hearing the cries of hunger and illness from his family, and stare for hours into the dirty yellow flood. Trying again to find work, and returning empty, he was apt to be more prolonged in his prayers. At other times, especially when there was work and a little food, he could read calmly from the Bible to the family.

Jim and his brother ventured from this slum to deliver laundry for their mother, and were beaten by roving gangs of white toughs. Instead of staying home in fear, Jim learned to outsmart the toughs, dodging around their favorite streets, and he became more venturesome. Here, it seemed, he had begun his long education in converting adversity into opportunity, and snatching accomplishment from hopelessness.

Jim was bolstered by his maternal grandfather, who had bashed his slave master with a rock at a garden party, when the master ridiculed him to a clergyman, and had run away. Grandfather had taught himself to read and write, had a vigorously political mind, and fascinated Jim with stories about Negro heroes. The Robinson family of four moved in with the grandparents, in a better section of town, before Jim entered his teens. His grandfather became a more constant influence, and Jim took to reading ravenously. During this same period, he met and greatly admired a sporty, eloquent Baptist clergyman, Jim Haywood.

"He preached my kind of gospel: work hard, never say die, have faith in yourself, don't let white folks fool you because you're as good as they, prayer is good but you've to be practical also."

When alone, Jim said, he would sometimes stride back and forth, imitating the preacher's sermons. On one such occasion, on a hot summer day in the park, his imagination turned the rippling brook into organ music and the bushes into nodding parishioners. In the middle of his "sermon," filled with urgent phrases about social justice, he was hailed by three Negro men who were lying beneath a tree, sharing a bottle of whiskey. At first, they taunted him.

Then one of them smashed the liquor bottle violently on a rock and told him: "Boy, get the hell out of here or you'll end up just like us. Ain't nothin', don't want nothin'." Jim knew the self-hatred of these men for what it was. He had felt it himself.

A vital nexus was forming within him at this period. There was the early core of love and devotion in his family, which persisted through quarrels and desperation. The biblical stories, such as those about Noah and his wife in the flood, or Abraham and Sarah in times of hunger, gave Jim a larger referent in faith and history—helped turn and open his mind to the searching, knowing, and strengthening God of history. The cruelty and beating that Jim received from white gangs also had referents in biblical stories of persecution, which stressed endurance, divine calling, and redemption from bondage.

All this helped provide a context of faith for the urgent note of social justice and the stories of particular racial heroes, such as Booker T. Washington, who had overcome adversity to forge lives of great worth and service. Finally, many of these factors were drawn together in the compelling image of Jim Haywood, the handsome, well-dressed and almost charismatic preacher with his combined message of biblical lore, steady courage, and betterment—but without the exclusivism and incoherent antics that Jim had come to abhor in the "Sanctified Church."

He developed stamina and cooperation, Jim recalled, by participating in a Negro youth gang that retaliated against white gangs by beating them up. It was the crude justice of "an eye for an eye, a tooth for a tooth." Yet through these sorties with "Tommy's gang," Jim reflected, he found "a feeling of worth and importance. And I learned to control my temper, to wait my time." Then came a key incident:

They beat up some whites. As Jim looked down at a white youth he was beating, he suddenly saw "the Negro" in the boy's face—the same sick terror that he had felt when he had been similarly beaten by whites. This sobering confrontation with himself, in the face of a white, gave Jim an early and indelible lesson that began his long education in compassion, and helped foster his warm feeling for the basic humanness of men.

Jim's mind jumbled the years, to the time he heard the

news of Pearl Harbor and "shook all over." He suddenly remembered the beatings by white gangs, and the time he was passed over for an R.O.T.C. commission in favor of whites with lower grades. He wanted to shout that it was a white man's war that Negroes should shun. Then because of his maturing education in patient endurance and compassion during later boyhood and college, he found himself flooded with other memories. "Despite all the hardship my white countrymen had enforced upon me, I still loved this land, its soil and people, with a fierce passion." He was swept by the words of the Lincoln University song: "For we love every inch of thy sacred soil, every tree on thy campus green. . . . "

Jim's family moved to Cleveland, where Jim hoped for an open society but found patterns of segregation. His thirst for learning continued, and had to be pursued secretly: His father opposed it, seeing no point in education. He felt a Negro would never have a chance to use it. He tried sternly to teach his son "his place" as a second-class citizen, but this lesson Jim refused to learn. He took morning and evening jobs, such as cleaning a barbershop and racking balls in a pool hall, and attended school in between, without his father's knowledge. He was pleasantly surprised to find little prejudice at Cleveland's Fairmont High. But every time his father found that Jim was attending school, he pulled the boy out. Then Jim would manufacture an address and try another school, and the story would be repeated. In two years, he completed one semester. Twice, he was within three weeks of finishing a semester when his father pulled him out.

Jim decided to leave home. It was a windy winter evening, and he recalled that the streets were dirty with slush and the sewers clogged. He finally found a job, "taking care of the furnace and sidewalk for a miserly colored woman." But he refused to fawn obsequiously for her, and that ended the job. In the following days, looking for work, he had almost no food. His clothes were in rags, and he was unwashed and "felt half alive." When the hunger became an urgent desperation, he begged or stole from fruit carts. Finally, he found an odd job.

Jim eked out an existence at any job he could find, going threadbare and weary to school, rarely having enough to eat, and often having nothing. (When he finally reached college, and was offered a job in the kitchen or yard, Jim recalled with a grin, he replied "the kitchen!" and almost flew through the roof with joy.) The jobs were impermanent, difficult to keep. For example, when he was running the night elevator in a men's club, he was seen with books by Spengler and Kant, which he read in his spare time. It seemed dangerous to his employers to have the elevator boy reading books of this kind, and he was fired.

Then, at the YMCA, he was befriended by one of the advisors, Ernest Escoe. Jim described him as a devout Methodist layman, tall and strong, and one who understood racial and political problems from a Christian perspective. He and his wife took Jim into their home, and the vigorous Escoe made a strong impression on Jim. It was in Escoe, Jim pondered, that he really saw how Christian faith could vitalize and hallow a man's life. There was a year of respite and smoother going; then relatives displaced Jim at the Escoe house, and he completed his senior year of school in the familiar pattern of jobs, hunger, and threadbare struggle.

After graduation, he lived for two winters on bread and beans with a kindly family that shared their home, but Jim hoped somehow to attend college. One day, he found work as a youth helper for a Congregational pastor. Through him, he met a roving Presbyterian leader, who introduced him to this church and the prospect of a modest grant from its Christian Education Fund. In due time, he was headed for Lincoln University with high hopes, some promises, and more than $100 to get him registered and started.

En route, his pocket was picked. All but $2.50 was gone. His eyes started with tears, and he felt "plowed under." A fellow bus passenger, a workman who spoke broken English, befriended him, urged him to go on, and gave him ten dollars. This man, a white, "restored my faith in people," Jim said. With $12.50 he went on.

Through a combination of daring, deception, and pleading, he was able to register at Lincoln in the fall of 1931. Given a job in the kitchen, he quickly gained fifty pounds and earned the nickname of Lead Belly. But he still had no money for tuition, let alone his personal needs, and was given the deadline of October 25. Again, it seemed the end. He brooded over it one blue October afternoon, standing on a railroad trestle, feeling dizzy, and watching the trains rush beneath.

Then, with sudden inspiration, he walked back to the library and took out the Minutes of the Presbyterian U.S.A. General Assembly (now the United Presbyterian Church in the U.S.A.). For two hours, it was the world's most val-

uable book to him, as he copied from it the names and ad-
dresses of all clergymen in the Cleveland area, and wrote
each one a brief request for help. By October 23 he had the
money. Four years later he emerged as valedictorian, a
leader in student politics and protests, and a star of the
debating team. On the final day, when accounts were
balanced, the bursar refunded to him $13.75. "On an in-
vestment of $12.50," he remarked wryly, "I had not only
gotten an education but had even made a dollar and a
quarter profit."

It was during one of his college summers, while he was
preaching at a church in Beardon, Tennessee, that he was
almost lynched by a howling white mob, angry and fear-
ful at the social justice emphasis in his sermons. Jim es-
caped because the mob stumbled on a little boy, and
vented its rage by beating the boy to death. This allowed
the few minutes that were necessary for an anonymous
white man to dash into the church, urge Jim into his
waiting car, and roar away.

Jim was bent on the ministry, vibrating with a young
man's desire to turn faith into action for brotherhood. Fi-
nancial help began to come from a woman he had never
seen. He simply received a letter one day, addressing him
as "my minister boy" and signed "your fairy godmother."
With her help he attended Union Theological Seminary in
New York, where at first he was shunned for racial reasons.
He was drastically disappointed at this collapse of his hal-
lowed hope for brotherhood in the halls of Christian
scholarship, and packed his bags one afternoon. But before
he left, he visited Professor Eugene Lyman, whose encouragement sustained him. Gradually he was accepted,

and finally admired and elected president of his class—that of 1938.

He also met the "fairy godmother," who turned out to be F. Lorraine Miller, a public school biology teacher in Tonawanda, New York, and a dedicated Christian. At one time, the entire Negro population of Tonawanda had been harried out of town. As an act of atonement, Miss Miller devoted what earnings she could to helping Negro students. Jim is only one of a number of clergymen, teachers, social workers, and others who are Miss Miller's "graduates." In 1955, he became the first Negro to deliver the Lyman Beecher lectures at Yale Divinity School.

From seminary graduation until he gave these lectures, there were seventeen years of quiet slogging as he converted his peculiar talents and concerns into action. He founded and pastored the Church of the Master, in the Morningside section of Manhattan. He was a practical integrationist who aimed at brotherhood under God. He found support from students and faculty members at nearby Union and Columbia University, and forged an integrated church and ministry. As a result, he was denounced for "bringing in the whites" by one Negro member, who left in high dudgeon with a few others.

Jim also founded the Morningside Community Center with its youth work, and later developed camps for needy city children on land that was loaned for the purpose in New Hampshire. Active in civic affairs, he was the driving force behind the acceptance of at least some Negro doctors in New York hospitals. He also ran for Manhattan Borough president on the liberal ticket, but decided that he couldn't be both a good pastor and a good politician.

But his interests have focused most consistently on young people. His severe struggles as a youth have been transformed into a passionate concern. This underlay his long, intermittent wrangle with the administrations of private colleges and universities about their admission policies toward Negro students. After repeated talks and investigations, he charged that many northern colleges and universities were unprejudiced only in theory, and in fact discouraged Negro applicants. The deans and presidents replied sharply that qualified Negroes didn't apply. Jim retorted by pointing to Negroes who had tried to apply, and to policies of excluding Negro students from dormitories. The situation gradually began to thaw, and Jim found a way to assist qualified Negro students when he helped to organize the National Scholarship Fund for Negro Students.

For his efforts, and his tendency to "knock a bung out of things," he was called some harsh names—including "Communist." The accusation was incredible. Jim had resolutely hit at all efforts to cramp, segregate, oppress, belittle, or in any way hold down human beings or limit their development. He believed deeply in individual redemption, freedom, dignity, and service under the fatherhood of God, and showed a strong streak of patriotism. Moreover, he had been cleared for government work.

Jim's drive developed the Crossroads project in 1957. The need to foster friendly relations between America and Africa—"the land of tomorrow morning"—had become so urgent, he said, that "we had to do something, over and above the dedicated work of our missionaries." He spoke briefly of traditional mission work, as a leading and familiar figure in missionary circles. He surveyed African missions in the summer of 1954. "When missionaries first went to Africa, a century or so ago, their life expectancy in the tropical areas was about five years." His voice became slower, reflective. "You can see their graves, along the trails to the inland settlements and in the high rain forests." Yet the Christian mission inaugurated 80 percent of the education south of the Sahara, and gave the legacy of an awakening continent.

And the awakened continent, he continued, "needed a new kind of effort, something which leapt beyond the traditional ways to influence American-African relations." The poet underscored the hope and daring of the man. Most people would scoff at the thought that one person with an idea and no money could really influence the relationship between two continents of people. But Jim saw the need with an urgent clarity, and set to work.

He visualized summer work camps composed of young Negro and white Americans, recruited from colleges, and working with young Africans on village projects, at the invitation of African governments. Most young Americans would pay their travel expenses. But there was still the cost of arrangements and projects. Jim faced one obstacle after another, such as governments to be dealt with by an almost unknown clergyman, red tape to be cut, helpers to be found. He looked for the opportunities in each obstacle. The lack of funds—"we had nothing, really nothing for money"—he accepted as a familiar challenge. Enlisting the aid of Rabbi Israel Mowshowitz of Jamaica, Queens, he approached religious groups, wealthy individuals, and foundations, gradually raising funds.

"You see," he explained briskly, his eyes wide and smiling, "I knew from working with students, building camps in New Hampshire, that they had a real opportunity to make a contribution in the world. I didn't pretend that they could transform the underdeveloped lands physically by building some schools or roads or water systems. They could simply do what they could, with their talents—and also with a deeper purpose. American and African students can relate and discover each other in a basic way, by working on a project together. And the African students of today are the leaders of tomorrow in their countries. Even when we help educate them, we still need to influence their understanding and hearts."

The smile around his eyes crinkled into irony. He was familiar, he indicated, with the stories of African students who were schooled in American colleges but weren't welcomed into American homes. Returning to their lands with bitter feelings about American racial practices, they had fertile hearts for the seeds of Communist influence. "Race prejudice exists, and I'd scarcely deny that," he continued, with now only an inflection of irony in his voice and smile to suggest the lashes he had felt. "Yet there's another side to the story, a side that's getting better with the years.

"But in Africa, a lot of the people get the impression from the papers that this country is one Little Rock from coast to coast. So we took an interracial, interfaith group of students to Africa, to work on specific projects. We included some southern whites, and we made sure to have whites and Negroes in each working group. We got African students to work with us in equal numbers. And we lived with them and their leaders. This was designed as a mission, a working testimony to the greatest democratic ideals of our Christian heritage. We also learned things about Africa and its people, and about ourselves."

Jim forged a concentrated effort in Africa. He made the camps interfaith as well as interracial, like ideal models of the American community at work. He selected leaders who could intelligently express their faith and convictions. He seized upon projects which, though small, were crucial to the people of an area—a water system, or a library to serve hundreds of square miles. But, unlike technical specialists sent by government, Crossroads' participants are committed to complete sharing, Americans and Africans living and working together. Also, Jim had an eye for including young Africans who seemed bent for political and civil service careers in their nations. Thus, at the crucial time when new nations were coming into being, he inaugurated something that he hoped would act as a lever on history. The projects would not be influential for their size or cost, but for being just the right thing, at the right moment, to give a twist of understanding and friendship to American-African relations.

To accomplish his purpose, he knew it was equally important to influence the United States with the African story. He found this difficult, the poet realized, because America is a developed society, with thousands of competent spokesmen for different views, and with a tiny fraction of its college students bound for key government posts. (By contrast, African students of the 1960's are an elite minority who must fill the leadership hunger of their lands.) However, Jim said, every effort is made "to spread the word of understanding in this country." All American participants in Crossroads, upon returning, are obliged to tell of their experiences in public speaking and writing. "Now, you can have a look," and he handed the poet a pamphlet with a roundup of student comments. Opening at random, the poet found these sentences from a San Antonio, Texas, lad:

"It is necessary for me . . . to say that before I went to Africa I was a prime example of a complacent American youth. I have never been interested in politics, economics, government, or foreign affairs. Now, having been introduced to the freshest of nationalism, I can only reverse my views. One can hardly come away from such an experience without being moved."

The first Crossroads project, in the summer of 1958, took sixty American students to five countries in Africa. They worked with African students on schools, roads, water systems, and the like. Money donated by individuals, religious and fraternal groups, and foundations was supplemented, and still is, by many of the students themselves who must pay some $900—about half the individual cost. They take this from their own pockets or raise it from campus or religious groups.

Warm endorsement for the project came from President Eisenhower, Peter Rudder, Ambassador to Ghana, and others. Yet "we had to skip the 1959 summer," Jim added, "because we didn't have enough money and owed a debt in Africa, which we had to pay before we went back again." But in 1960 the Crossroaders returned to Africa, 180 strong in ten countries. The next year there were 191 in fourteen countries. The following years brought substantial increases in Crossroads participants and projects.

The invitations from African governments also increased.

There are plenty of capable students who are eager to go, Jim indicated. They are first screened by their colleges and universities, then by the project itself. After final screening and selection, they are assigned to read books on African history, cultures, geography, and the like. Then they are coached rigorously for a week in New York before departing. The amount of difficulty from physical ills or emotional disturbance among the Crossroaders, suddenly transplanted to hard work and sparse living in an alien environment, has been practically nil—a record that speaks as well for American youth as for the screening and coaching processes. Jim is helped by a small permanent staff, with his wife Gertrude as executive assistant. They were married in 1958. They have no children, and live modestly in Morningside Gardens, a cooperative housing project near Columbia University.

A few years after he started with "nothing for money," and an idea for affecting the course of history, Jim could speak about results. Crossroaders, returning to America, had been ambassadors for understanding with Africa. African students who worked with Crossroads had gone on to important government posts. Jim names several at random: William Fitzjohn, ambassador from Sierra Leone to Great Britain; Johnson Appiah, first secretary of the Ghana Mission to the United Nations; John Marc Ehoh, minister of education in Gabon; and "we were befriended by E. M. Debrah of Ghana, who became first secretary of his country's embassy in Washington." Then he briefly recounted some anecdotes to suggest the African appreciation of Crossroads.

Ambassador of Brotherhood

On Independence Day in Ghana, Prime Minister Nkrumah took the American students to the celebration in his own bus. In Liberia, President Tubman traveled twelve hours over rugged roads in the rainy season to dedicate a library the students had built. In a village in Dahomey, where the students used sleeping bags and tents, the chief told them warmly that other whites had always used the hotels; but "you have come to join with us in a way nobody ever has." When that country became independent, the Crossroaders were the private guests of the Prime Minister, the greatest honor he could bestow. Jim skipped to another incident, then another, the stories tumbling on each other.

As he did so, the poet pondered the tough, compassionate power that had been packed into the stocky man opposite him. Jim folded his hands on the desk now, his eyes warm with humor, and his voice calmly urgent:

"I feel that every individual has a basic responsibility to do as much as he can. People get stymied by the fact that there's so much to be done, and they're so little, and can do only a small share of it. So they refuse to do what they can. But that, I think, negates the whole point that Jesus was making in the parable of the talents.

"Look, it wasn't the five talent man or the two talent man that he was basically concerned about, though he was thinking of them. But the trouble was the one talent man, who took his talent and buried it in the ground. And you see, there are so many, many more of us one talent people than two or five talent people that if each of us would live up only to what he could do, this would make a tremendous wedge in the world."

· 6 ·

Physician to the Whole Person

AH, GENEVA! The poet had dined by candlelight in a little cellar cafe, tramped through snow on the Rue du Mont Blanc, slept under a feather quilt a foot thick, breakfasted on croissants with preserves and a slab of cheese, and now sat in the study of Paul Tournier, M.D., the man who had become a physician to the whole person. It was a winter of extraordinary snows in Europe, and the steady flakes fell softly onto green fir trees outside the tall windows of the study. Dr. Tournier touched a match to the fuel in the fireplace, which occupied a corner between the bookcase wall and the windows opposite.

The doctor was a large-boned man, kneeling there on the hearth and fanning the flame to get it well started. He saw his patients here, across the glow of firelight. He felt the fire was important, its warmth and light helping to generate a dialogue between persons—an insight as old as mankind, dating back to primitive Peking Man.

Physician to the Whole Person

Now they sat, Dr. Tournier with his back to the bookcase and facing the poet across the glowing hearth. A little to one side there sat a noted Swiss pastor, alertly acting as translator. Dr. Tournier was hesitant in speaking English, and the poet had had only two years of high school French, which he had long since forgotten. He was sorry about this language barrier. It had been a blank wall between him and the waitress in the cafe where he dined, and he had finally ordered in sign language.

Now he urgently wanted to converse directly with the doctor, sitting opposite. Dr. Tournier's thinning gray hair grew in a couple of big shocks above his temples. He sat with legs protruding in front of him and his feet squarely on the floor. His large, rugged, and almost drooping features held an unusual smile. It wasn't a smile *on* his face. In the usual sense, it was only sometimes a smile. But consistently, it was an expression that welled into the face, carrying warmth, humor, and a kind irony.

Among physicians and psychologists in America, Dr. Tournier was liked ardently, or criticized sharply, or supported with both warmth and reservations. He was a physician turned psychiatrist, and in his several books he brought a psychological, biblical, and medical perspective to illness and health. To prepare for the interview, the poet had read some of Dr. Tournier's work, expecting to find a lot of intellection, with a precise pursuit and definition of ideas. Instead, he found books that were more like a dialogue. Opening their pages was like pulling up his chair to a cafe table and listening to a conversation. It was a Swiss scientist's version of John Hayes' "sort-of talk," revealed especially in *The Meaning of Persons*.

Now, the object was to sense and reflect the quality of the inner person, which was always difficult, and seemed impossible with the language barrier. Facts about a person were not the same as the inner truths of the person. Facts could help reveal—or disguise—these inner truths. Still, one started with facts. Dr. Tournier gave facts honestly and intimately, which was a real help.

With his head held slightly to one side and his large features relaxed, Dr. Tournier related that he had been born in Geneva in 1898, and had one older sister. His father, pastor of the National Protestant Cathedral, died when he was three months old. His mother died when he was six. He had almost no memories of these years, though he recalled that he was a lonely child. His description gave the impression of someone warmly and simply bringing forth an old intimacy. After his mother died, he went to live with his aunt and uncle. His uncle was benevolent, in an impersonal way. His aunt was mentally ill, with a delusion, and used to keep her luggage packed with Bibles. Dr. Tournier related these things with the ease and sincerity that someone might use in saying, "When I was young we had a wonderful old dog," except that he wasn't talking about dogs.

There was emerging a drastic contradiction between Dr. Tournier and the background he described. Was there no one who during his childhood had provided consistent love, had given consistent warmth and affection? Without this, modern psychology maintained—with a lot of evidence—that a child could not grow to be warm and loving. The child would withdraw, shrinking into himself. From the environment Dr. Tournier described, a child might easily become insane, or at best grow to be cold and impersonal, one of those people whose warmth drained completely away from the face and skin. But Dr. Tournier, lounging in his chair across the hearth, seemed exactly the opposite—a person of brimming warmth.

"I became very withdrawn," Dr. Tournier stated. By the age of thirteen or fourteen, he related, he was so cold and withdrawn that, when he entered a group, the conversation would die. He felt isolated, wanting friends, and he would join this or that group of schoolmates. Even if he said nothing, the conversation would die. There was no active dislike between him and these schoolmates. He simply exerted a freezing influence.

For a time he was a poor student, except in math—cold clarity, the poet reflected. His uncle feared that he would fail intellectually, and enrolled him in woodworking classes. But soon his studies improved, and by the age of seventeen he became an outstanding student and intellectual leader. At the College of Calvin, and then at the University of Geneva, he could talk to others and even dominate them by his intellectual learning and precision. But there was no warmth in these encounters. The real *person* lived a withdrawn life, and the poet sensed what Dr. Tournier was saying before it was quite translated.

"The person hides behind the personage, the outer fabrication of himself," Dr. Tournier generalized, speaking through their interpreter. "It is difficult to go beyond the personage and establish genuine dialogue. A person runs from dialogue and creates a personage, because he is afraid of discovering and revealing his person as it really is."

Dr. Tournier blew his large nose, stretched his feet a bit closer to the fire, and resumed. He told about a professor of Greek who took an interest in him. The professor was idealistic and spiritual in his interests, and regarded God as an impersonal ultimate. He could not pray, because prayer could be said only to a personal God. He was not a Christian. But he did form a personal association with Paul Tournier—and the doctor kept talking about this, shifting in his chair by the fireside and talking about the Greek professor. Evidently, this was the first experience of a close human association that he could remember. But it wouldn't have made a significant difference, because life was already too stacked against him.

He was graduated from the University of Geneva with the finest examination results in thirty years. He was an isolated, coldly brilliant young man who had a tendency to dominate others. He attended church, and later one pastor told him, "You must read Calvin." He did so, was impressed by Calvin's intellectual weight, and became a champion of the reformer. But Dr. Tournier's convictions were intellectual, not warm and personal.

Yet his instincts were humanitarian. During his student years, he worked with the Red Cross and the Save the Children Fund. He became a physician—wanting subconsciously, he said, to avenge his mother's death by healing others. "I became a doctor for the person, not the science," Dr. Tournier elaborated. The poet, listening with all the doors of his attention open, noted down the gist of the remark before the interpreter had rendered the words into English. Then Dr. Tournier related that he was married in 1924, a year after graduation, when he was working in hospitals in Paris. In 1928, he started a general practice in Geneva.

They enjoyed a moment of silence. The poet felt his feet warmed outwardly from the fire, but felt the rest of him more subtly warmed by the talk and presence of the man opposite. He thought of Bonhoeffer's description of God as "the Beyond in our midst."

Dr. Tournier resumed. His spiritual interests had deepened, he said, via a Christian friend, and he became involved in the affairs and modern reform of the church. He responded intellectually, but in his inner heart and person he remained isolated. Then, through one of his patients, he encountered the Oxford Movement. He became friends with one of its leaders, a Dutch official at the League of Nations.

They exchanged life stories, with Dr. Tournier unburdening himself. It was his first experience of deep personal contact, warmer and more personal than his association with the professor of Greek. The thawing of the inner person had begun. He began the discipline of quiet times and prayer every day. He and his wife had happy relationships, he said—though the poet wondered how happy it had been with the inner character of Dr. Tournier withdrawn. As Christians, they had worked to build a Christian home, and tried praying together. But he tended to dominate and preach at his wife, which she did not appreciate.

Now, however, they began a new sort of quiet time. They prayed, invoking the guidance of God. Then, they *wrote* to each other. This doctor and his wife, who shared the same bedroom and were by then the parents of two sons, had to write to each other to begin sharing in a deep way. It took a quiet, solid courage for a person to face openly and acknowledge such isolation and need.

Dr. Tournier didn't recall what he wrote in this first quiet time together. But he recited word for word his wife's first message, and the interpreter questioned the easygoing words. *"Mais oui, oui,"* Dr. Tournier replied, with the resonance of an ironic chuckle in his voice as he repeated what his wife had written to him:

"You have been my professor and pastor, but not my husband. . . . Now I can help you."

So began a deep sharing between husband and wife. Its effects reverberated into Dr. Tournier's professional life. Soon, patients started to tell Dr. Tournier their personal troubles. They *felt*, now, that they could. He invited them to his home in the evening to talk. He was becoming a doctor to the whole person.

In study and prayer, he deepened both his spiritual life and his knowledge of psychology. To this day he has continued the practice of quiet times, with and without his wife. (He dropped from the Oxford Movement when it later spawned Moral Rearmament.) He felt himself strongly inclined from medicine toward psychology, and considered studying in Zurich with an eminent psychoanalyst who was a friend of Freud and Jung.

"We have many psychoanalysts," the doctor wrote back to him in reply to a letter of inquiry, "but only one Paul Tournier."

Warmth seemed to brim from the man as he lounged in his chair by the hearth. He was clearly pleased, with an expression that carried a boyish overtone. He did not back away from his Christian uniqueness, just as he hadn't tried to disguise his spiritual isolation. He related that he remained in Geneva and sought the will of God for his life. He realized that his mission was to bring his medical knowledge together with his personal and psychological insight, using both in an essentially biblical perspective, and being a doctor to the whole person.

"So I began devoting myself to the relation between moral, medical, and spiritual man," Dr. Tournier continued. The morality enters, he explained, in the constant, daily choices one makes in personal relations. And this applies very much to people who worship the God of love. He gave the example of a woman who came to him, troubled by a problem in her home. "I asked her what her husband thinks about this, and she replied, 'My husband! As soon as I try to talk to him seriously about anything, he picks up his hat and goes off to his club!'"

He added that some men use their tiredness, at the end of a day's work, to screen themselves from intimate conversation. Some women do the same, and may hold their children back by saying that Daddy is too tired, and should be left alone. Some married couples have a subtle, unspoken conspiracy to be frequently in the company of friends, to keep busy with community or church activities, so as to avoid confronting and knowing each other intimately, as persons. He cited brief examples from his psychiatric practice, speaking thoughtfully and culling the examples from his roomy memory.

So his deepest pain—personal isolation—was transformed to his greatest strength as a doctor. For Dr. Tournier seemed to know every dodge that people use to avoid intimate talk and inner growth. "Sometimes a husband or wife doesn't know what to say, when a certain subject is discussed," he was saying. "They shift the talk to something more comfortable, repressing what they may need most to discuss. Some are afraid of the emotions a topic may arouse. Yet we need to be emotionally honest. . . ."

He was talking earnestly, gesturing quietly with his large hands. He recalled that his experiences naturally developed into his first book, *Médecin de la Personne* (untranslated at the time). He was forty-two when he wrote it. He took the manuscript to the professor of Greek who had been sympathetically interested in him. The professor told him to go ahead and read it aloud.

Dr. Tournier had begun reading. The professor did not interrupt him. Dr. Tournier read through a chapter of the book. At the end, the professor said, "Paul, we must pray together."

"You are a Christian?" Dr. Tournier had asked in surprise.

"Yes."

"But from when?"

"From now."

The book attracted considerable interest among European doctors. With the help of the interest it aroused, Dr. Tournier was instrumental in founding an international, interfaith group of physicians who meet to discuss the healing of the whole person. The meetings rotate among European countries. The group has steadily grown in membership and influence, and works as a humanizing and spiritual leaven in the medical profession.

The group has members from Communist lands. "And

there is an interesting thing," the doctor pursued, leaning forward. "The Westerners in our group say that one can be a non-Christian and be a physician to the whole person. But the doctors from Communist countries say no, you must be a Christian to minister to the whole person. A few years ago, a Communist member of the group said he had never found such brotherhood before, not even in the Communist party." The poet remembered John Hayes, working with an attitude of Christian love in China and influencing Communists because he was sincerely interested in their welfare as persons.

Dr. Tournier again mentioned ways in which people hide from genuine dialogue, creating personal and international barriers. The barrier builders, his discussion indicated, are the people who inwardly are more afraid. In contrast, the missionary went forth himself, in a deeply personal way made practical in his or her daily affairs—medical practice, marriage bed, Communist prison, care of children—it was the power of the genuinely personal, the Christ power of giving from the self. "Personal relations" —the phrase was taking a resonant, exciting meaning in Dr. Tournier's discussion.

The doctor referred frequently to his wife, and several times to their two sons: Jean Louis, who works with the government's Postal Telephone and Telegraph, and Gabriel, an architect. The doctor added that he does not see a full caseload of patients anymore. He described his day as follows:

He rises at 6:30 A.M., and goes for breakfast at 7 A.M. in a downtown cafe. Here he has coffee and croissants, reads the newspaper, and spends twenty minutes in prayer and meditation. Then, still at his cafe table, he reads his mail and spends an hour or so writing his current book. He likes to work and meditate in the cafe because he is in the midst of people, informally in touch with many lives. At 10 A.M. he goes back to the office, and sees patients for the rest of the day. On Tuesdays he stays all morning in the cafe, answering his backlog of mail.

Aside from normal holidays, he breaks this schedule a week each year for the international, interfaith conference on medicine for the whole person. For fifteen years, Dr. Tournier has been the one person entrusted by all to lead the Bible studies. He takes a specific problem, such as an illness, and throws the light of the Bible upon it. A Spanish physician translated his *Doctor's Casebook in the Light of the Bible,* and after seven years it received the imprimatur of the Roman Catholic Church in Spain and was published there. It was another instance of crossing barriers and joining with others.

Being a physician to the whole person, Dr. Tournier explained, "isn't a technique that can be taught, but rather flows from a transformation in the physician. He must become a responsible person before God and man." The doctor spoke firmly, leaning forward to make his point, his face underlain by his warming expression.

And the poet, drawn toward the man and listening intently, wrote down Dr. Tournier's reply quite accurately.

"I see you have begun catching Paul's French," the interpreter remarked. "Yet we understand that you didn't know French."

"He is understanding some now," Dr. Tournier remarked.

It had really happened. This man, who once had frozen conversation by his very presence, had so drawn the poet with his warmth and sympathy that the language barrier itself had begun to crumble. Now the poet's French lessons of years before, layered over in the memory, had been unlocked and come alive. It was an outward, psychologically explainable sign of a deeper power: the grace of God, mediated through Dr. Tournier.

Now, as he saw Dr. Tournier sitting easily and attentively opposite him, he felt the significance of a remark to the doctor by one of his patients: "You are implacable!" And Dr. Tournier had explained: "I wasn't pressing the patient with questions at all. I was listening, with all the intense attention that a struggling soul deserves." In his very listening, there was something implacable, thawing a person and drawing him out. American psychologists have a name for such a person: "the healing personality."

The interview continued somewhat during a charming lunch with Mrs. Tournier. That afternoon, while Dr. Tournier saw some patients across the fireside in his study, the poet toured Geneva with the English-speaking pastor, then tramped the streets alone, giving directions in French to some lost tourists, and finally ordering his dinner with no difficulty.

The dialogue with Dr. Tournier resumed that evening at the poet's hotel, and they talked on the personal level, of their work and concerns. The poet indeed felt something implacable about this man with his large, rugged features. He did feel that Dr. Tournier sometimes had to work at the dialogue, and hesitated to use his modest English. He also felt that Dr. Tournier's forte was less in psychiatric theory than in the power of his personal presence.

For he had a warm attentiveness that drew the poet out, and fostered an inner glow of ease and freedom. They shared coffee and cheese, and Dr. Tournier sometimes leaned close to listen to the poet. When the doctor made a statement, he had a way of pausing, his lower lip puffed forward slightly in the suggestion of a smile and his mind open to any response. A true dialogue, the doctor indicated, occurs between persons because each lives in relation with God, whether he acknowledges this or not. This prior and continuing relation makes a communion between persons possible. They talked like this for nearly two hours, the dialogue shuttling between them, and the hours went like twenty minutes.

And it was time to go, each having a schedule to keep.

The snow was still falling softly in the light from the cafe, and falling softly on the broad shoulders of Dr. Tournier as he walked away, framed for a moment in the lights from the Rue du Mont Blanc, and as the poet watched him he thought of the legendary words in a Christmas carol:

> "Heat was in the very sod
> Which the saint had printed."

· 7 ·

Mission at Oak Ridge

"I GUESS God was pretty dead for me—so dead that I didn't even bother with the question." The speaker was Dr. William G. Pollard, the squarely-built and genial director of the Oak Ridge Institute of Nuclear Studies, a project of southern universities devoted solely to the peaceful development of atomic energy.

He was talking with the poet in his spacious office in Oak Ridge, where he sat in a comfortable leather armchair, smoking his pipe, and speaking reflectively. Outside, God's good sunshine was shimmering warmly on the new leaves of early April.

"My family were churchgoers," Dr. Pollard related. "I was born in Batavia, New York, but we moved to Knoxville when I was twelve. My father was an engineer, and he became the representative for an electrical equipment firm in this area. The family went to church, and I went to Sunday school.

"I had no specific arguments against God. It was just that the positive developments left God out. There was no place or need for religious faith, it seemed. By the time I got to the University of Tennessee, I'd pretty well shed any faith I'd had."

"It sounds like a carefree youngster shedding his clothes at the swimming hole," the poet suggested. On his inner eye, he saw the image of young Dr. Pollard cheerfully peeling off a paper religion, consisting of a few layers of Sunday school leaflets, mission stories, and cardboard cutouts—the very things that had helped a genuine faith come easily to Dr. Nida.

"This was pretty much the story," Dr. Pollard said. "I entered the university during the heyday of materialism and determinism on the campuses. These ideas pervaded everything, even the liberal arts. In philosophy, Professor Axel Brett was a strong influence on me. His views were pretty much materialistic and deterministic. Nobody cared about God. He was so dead for me, and for a lot of my contemporaries entering the sciences, that we didn't even care about the questions. If religion was mentioned at all, it was shrugged off as a vestigial superstition."

As Dr. Pollard elaborated on the "death of God" for his generation of scientists, the contrast between Dr. Nida and Dr. Pollard became clearer. Both were sons of solid, churchgoing, middle-class parents, and had attended Sunday school. Here, Christianity met the developing interests and talents of young Dr. Nida. The cutouts met his interest in making and shaping things, and the stories met his interest in people and mission work. But Dr. Pollard and the other fledgling scientists had been interested in how material reality worked; the functioning of cells, reacting of chemicals, and the properties of atoms. And Christianity had not met the scientists there. For some reason, it had not joined with them. So the generation of physicists who made the atom bomb had learned to live without knowing the Creator who had given birth to the atoms.

"There was a wave of confidence in science," Dr. Pollard was saying. He stoked his pipe, lit it, and continued: "We just rode on this wave of confidence—science would solve everything—and God was out. I got my Ph.D. at Rice Institute in 1936, then came back to the University of Tennessee as an assistant professor in physics. I still held the materialist view. By this time, no other view seemed relevant or even possible."

But a gradual change began in him.

"My wife came from a strong religious background. I felt that the only rational way to make the best of our material universe was to comprehend its material nature. But she kept asking me to go with her to church on Sundays. It caused some difficult times.

"I finally did go to church," he continued, "simply to keep peace in our home. It seemed the rational thing to do. But I hadn't changed my beliefs one iota. I didn't join in the prayers, and the Creed seemed quite ridiculous to me."

Dr. Pollard told how he had continued to go to church with his wife, in calm and confident disbelief, though he did begin singing some of the hymns—"I enjoyed singing." The pattern continued in New York, where in 1944 Dr.

Pollard was called to join Columbia University's Special Alloys and Metals Laboratory—the cover name for the Manhattan Project, which developed the atomic bomb. He got a house for the family in Mount Vernon, he indicated, and commuted to his secret work in the city, where he specialized in getting the explosive variant of uranium out of the common form of the element.

"We went to church," he continued, "but it didn't seem to mean anything more to me. I thought of myself as just a father taking his wife and four small boys somewhere on Sunday morning. My interest was in the work. We weren't told of the successful test in the New Mexico desert in July of forty-five. When President Truman announced the Hiroshima bomb a few weeks later, we were exhilarated. We kept the radio going most of the afternoon and kept running out to buy the latest papers. It was a great day for science.

"Then they dropped the bomb on Nagasaki a few days later.

"I felt . . . bad. I didn't feel guilty, because I had been doing my job as a physicist, and this wasn't something to feel guilty about. But I had the feeling that these bombs might be sprinkled all over the map. When I got home to Mount Vernon, I looked in the paper to see if there was an evening church service I could catch. There was, and I went. I still can't put my finger on exactly why."

He paused, puffing reflectively on his pipe, then continued.

"It didn't seem to make a significant difference. Come Sunday morning, I was still a father who was just taking his wife and children somewhere." He told how this pattern continued when the family returned to Knoxville, where he resumed his teaching job. He heard the physicist Dr. Katherine Way outline an idea for making the developments at the atomic city of Oak Ridge, thirty miles from Knoxville, available to university researchers. The idea seemed splendid to Dr. Pollard. He helped develop the Oak Ridge Institute of Nuclear Studies.

In 1947 he quit his secure teaching job to become executive director of this new project. Under his leadership, it has grown into a research program, training program, medical program, and museum program.

In Oak Ridge, he found himself heading a building fund drive for a new church. Later, he superintended the Sunday school: "I had four children in it. I couldn't refuse." Because of his Sunday school work, he began to delve into Christianity seriously, and found its scholarship "just as fine in its own field and tradition as the scholarship of physics."

His impulse to go to church, after the Nagasaki bomb, suggested that an inner basis for Christian commitment had been forming. Now he continued to study, with his conviction growing, until he decided to systematize his knowledge in a professional manner. So he studied for the ministry in his spare time at Oak Ridge. In effect, Dr. Pollard developed a Christian outlook in the same methodical way that he had become a physicist, a way that was in keeping with his training and inclinations. After passing some tough examinations, he was ordained a priest of the Protestant Episcopal Church.

"Some of my scientific colleagues were rather surprised,

though they accepted the decision. I informed the directors of the Institute, of course, and asked if they felt my ordination posed a problem. At the meeting, they asked me to leave the room—the usual procedure, when a person is being considered by the directors. Then I was called back in, and told I was reelected." He grinned.

"It made me feel darned good! I enjoy this work thoroughly. The community of physics has its very legitimate field and concerns, as does the community of the church."

"What difference does it make to you, belonging to the Christian community?"

"Well . . . its perspective . . . it's. . . . " The scientific mind was groping for metaphors of the human spirit, and the poet tossed in a few suggestions, until Dr. Pollard finally said: "It was like blinders coming off. I'd been seeing a narrow portion of things. Now I got a fuller view. It opened up the whole range of reality. I think the richness of the experience was increased by my coming to it as a scientist, after learning what we know about our material world. I think my fellow scientists would feel the same." Yet he would deliver no sweeping judgments of the sciences. He loved his field, and in a nice way he indicated his disagreement with those who disparage the sciences. For a moment, he looked silently out one of the picture windows, across the citadel of scientific progressivism, where several big plants were carrying on a process crucial to the manufacture of modern superbombs. "The faiths that man erected on science seem pretty dubious," he remarked dryly.

On the bookcase by his desk, there was a small, beautifully-made scale model of a nuclear reactor. It was inscribed to Dr. Pollard by the Japanese. It signified their appreciation of him, for having started and headed a church commission that gave Japan a reactor for research into the peaceful uses of atomic energy. The reactor model seemed a sign and symbol of the transformation that had been patiently wrought in Dr. Pollard the bomb-maker, and the transformation that Dr. Pollard was now spreading far and wide, fostering the peaceful uses of atomic energy through the work of the Institute.

Half an hour later, in the modest Pollard home on the ridge of oak trees, Mrs. Pollard described her role in her husband's gradual conversion: "I got the body to church, and turned it over to the Lord. I guess it took about a year before he started saying 'amen' to some of the prayers, and I said to myself, well, we got a little farther this year. And it went on like that, bit by bit, getting a little farther every few years. . . . "

"Well," Dr. Pollard said, "well. . . . " The physicist, wearing his clericals, seemed a little abashed by the wifely frankness. To Mrs. Pollard, matters were quite direct and simple. Materialism was piffle, and she got her husband's body to church, and the Lord did the rest. The Pollards and their guest talked and chuckled as they sat in the living room, sipping a superb Tennessee refreshment made by the sour mash process, and looking out over a valley of budding oak trees and dogwoods in full blossom. The dogwoods grew in wild profusion, their flowers ivory-white in the late afternoon sun.

The Pollards began talking about their three sons. One was becoming a mathematician and physicist, another was becoming an anthropologist specializing in American

Indians, and a third was becoming a clergyman. All were strong Christians. But another name—"Jamie"—kept coming into their talk. He also was their son.

"He was going into the ministry," Dr. Pollard related. "He had something special, an enthusiasm. . . . "

"A verve. . . . " Mrs. Pollard said.

"Yes, I remember that Saturday in the summer, when Jamie was driving with me—I was coming home from some lectures. He was filled with ideas. He was talking about funerals. He felt there was a lot of paganism in modern funerals, and his analysis of the whole thing was keen. Then he started describing how a funeral service should be done. He went through the whole thing, saying just what should be said and sung; I sat there and listened.

"Three days later, he was riding with his brother in our little Metropolitan. They were driving down a straight stretch of road. It was uneven—under repair—but straight. We don't know what happened next, because it happened too fast. Someone here in Oak Ridge came over the hill, in the opposite direction, just in time to see our car bounding end over end down the road. Jamie was thrown clear, and died instantly with a broken neck.

"His brother had hardly a scratch. And he reacted courageously. He insisted on calling me himself, to tell me about Jamie. He went with me the next day, and we picked out an identical Metropolitan, and he drove it. He wasn't afraid. Jamie was buried with exactly the funeral he had described. It was a triumphant service."

"There were no flowers at the grave, no frills," Mrs. Pollard said with a smile. "There was just a nice, neat hole in the ground."

"On the next Wednesday," Dr. Pollard continued, "I celebrated the 6:30 A.M. communion service as usual, over at the church. I made it a memorial to Jamie. The memorial sentence is simply inserted briefly, into the regular service. We usually get about thirty people to this early service. But on this morning, they just kept coming, and coming"—the square-shouldered scientist could not repress a lump of emotion in his voice—"and 130 people came. It was a wonderful thing. A number of these friends established a scholarship fund as a memorial to Jamie. It's helping two students now, at General Seminary in New York."

The next morning, they toured the work of the Institute, the practical means for carrying forward the mission to transform people and situations with the mind of Christ —with love.

"The Institute now has a staff of 250," Dr. Pollard explained as they snapped on their seat belts in the little Metropolitan. "We're supported now by thirty-nine southern colleges and universities. The response has been gratifying. We give them research opportunities here at Oak Ridge and its laboratories. We also have a training division. We've trained quite a few people from this country, and from fifty-eight countries overseas. . . . " The people were trained in medical and other peaceful uses of atomic energy.

They drove to a nearby parking field.

"Now, here's our cancer research hospital. Thirty beds. We're working especially on leukemia now, trying to develop something in conjunction with other forms of therapy. We've shown progress, but no cures."

MEN FOR OTHERS

In the hospital, they walked down blue-gray corridors, through a heavy door that Dr. Pollard opened with his keys, and now there were red warning signs:

DANGER

RADIATION

They went through another door, into a control room, where they were joined by a hospital executive in white.

"This is our whole body radiation room," Dr. Pollard said. "We use it for leukemia. The radiologist sits here," and he pointed to a chair at a control panel, a big hand protruding from a sleeve of his clericals. "He watches the patient through this mirror."

The poet looked in the mirror and saw a bed, empty. It seemed to be right behind him. But behind him was a heavy wall, with another mirror. With Dr. Pollard leading, they walked around. Mirror followed mirror. The image of the bed was actually coming from directly in front of the control panel. The two were separated by a heavy wall. The system of mirrors allowed the radiologist to watch the patient, while remaining out of the radiation. The radiation room was nearly square, with a raised bed, and slots angling from different parts of the wall.

"The radiation comes from these slots," Dr. Pollard explained. "They are arranged so that the whole body is evenly radiated, as the patient lies full length on the bed. He can watch television during the radiation," and he pointed to a television set above the foot of the bed. "He operates the television with a remote control. A person can take one or possibly two of these doses."

"We like to stress," the hospital executive said, "that

the person has a period of useful life left as a result of the therapy."

Dr. Pollard thanked the hospital executive and led the way upstairs, into a lecture room. Here he described the standardizing of measures for radiation treatments. This was done by female mannequins, sawed off at the waist. They were given such names as Abigail and Bridget. Half a dozen were stacked neatly in a cabinet. "We ship these sawed off ladies around the country, with standard doses of radioactive iodine," Dr. Pollard explained. "Before we started this, all sorts of standards were being used for medical doses." He led the way to other rooms. Here there were detection machines, radiation "scanners" that pinpointed the locations of cancerous growths.

Then they drove to the Museum of Atomic Energy, another project of the Institute. "The museum also prepares traveling exhibits," Dr. Pollard explained. "We worked on the 'Atoms for Peace' display. These days, a couple of our popular exhibits are 'Your Stake in the Atom' and 'This Atomic World.' Schools and colleges use them."

In two lecture areas of the museum, staff men were giving talks. The children in one area seemed to be junior high school age, and the children in the other were about senior high age. The speakers worked with models and charts. The young people were asking about nuclear fuel, radiation effects, the possible relation between radiation and cell development, and the concept of probability: real questions that interested the school youngsters of today.

"The children are not from special schools of science," Dr. Pollard explained. "They're simply a couple of public school groups. We get them by the busload. Here, you can see some of the displays they've made," and he pointed to professional-looking exhibits to one side. The youngsters had been working with radiation detection and half a dozen other problems that used to be grist for college physics courses.

Dr. Pollard led the way around the museum, which displayed many uses for atomic energy. There was an array of industrial uses, such as the way a harmless potion of a radioactive substance could be employed to pinpoint a lead in a thousand miles of pipeline. There were medical uses and agricultural uses. Dr. Pollard talked and explained as he went. In his wake, a straggling crowd of museum visitors began to follow. Dr. Pollard didn't seem to notice the stragglers. His attention was moving enthusiastically along the familiar exhibits. The poet blended with the stragglers and listened to their conversation:

"You think he's the head of the museum, or something?"

"He can't be. He's a clergyman."

"No!"

"He is, too. Didn't you see him, Bill?"

"He's got his back to us. But it looked like a clerical collar."

"You two must be seeing things. The guy's a scientist. A clergyman wouldn't know an isotope from his elbow. They don't care about these things. . . . Well, I'll be doggoned!"

Dr. Pollard had paused in front of a big, illuminated panel, and turned around. His collar and broad shoulders in the black clericals were outlined sharply in the light from the yellow-green panel and behind him. He started to explain the exhibits briefly to the poet, and the straggling visitors paused to listen as well. "Project to eliminate fruit flies . . . male flies sterilized with radiation and released . . . male sterile with females . . . fruit fly population substantially down in the test area . . . crops a lot better. . . . "

"Any harmful side effects, as with the insecticides?"

"No. It's neat and completely clean . . . very limited application so far . . . you see, the fly's habits. . . . " He talked for a minute about the mating habits of flies, then went back to radiation effects, giving a brief and impromptu talk.

As he did so, the poet watched and listened to the whole exhibit—the man, the talk, the little scattering of people, and their talk:

"I never thought I'd see the day."

"What do you mean?"

"A really religious guy, here like this. I didn't think religion did anything in public, except for Billy Graham and whats-his-name—you know, the one with the name like beer."

"Peale."

"Yeah. What's he saying now?"

"The flies."

"He's *intelligent*."

Dr. Pollard seemed quite unaware of how closely he was being attended to. He finished, and went to another exhibit with the poet. One couple from the loose group came over to him.

"We were wondering who you are."

"William G. Pollard. Bill Pollard," he replied cordially. They talked for a moment. The couple went away still curious. Dr. Pollard had not said he was director of the Institute and hadn't otherwise publicized himself. He was not in this work for the status or power it might bring.

So there, in a nutshell, was Dr. Pollard's mission in the world: He worked with an Institute, using a hospital, using an academic research program, using a study program, and using a museum with lectures and exhibits, to gather the work of nuclear physics, transform this to dozens of beneficial uses, and breed these uses and their concepts of benevolence and peace into the world.

Ten minutes later, as they drove back toward the Institute, the poet began to press an avid discussion on scientific thinking and theology. In the car and for an hour in Dr. Pollard's office, the talk bounded along:

Origin of the universe on the verge of being dated . . . implicitly supports the First Cause idea of God . . . date will probably be around thirteen billion years ago, as the earth measures years . . . origin infers cause outside space and time . . . same thing for the explanation of small nuclear particles . . . dimensions of eternity intersect our four dimensions of space and time . . . run perpendicular to our space and time . . . quantum mechanics undercuts determinist position . . . suggests basis for Providence in the nature of things, in atomic structure itself. . . . Here for an hour were his insights, from the world to the church. They are set forth in more detail in his two books, *Chance and Providence,* and *Physicist and Christian*—the later chapters, especially.

In an age of science, when junior high schoolers were

cutting their intellectual teeth on material that seemed irrelevant or incomprehensible to most of their pastors, this man Pollard was *joining with* the community and data of science. He was transforming the material and was presenting it on the doorsteps of professional theologians for their attention and further efforts. And what was happening?

The poet wondered about this later, as he stood on the lawn outside his motel room, looking over the long valley and laboratories and atomic plants of Oak Ridge. Here was the citadel of worldly power that had changed history with a bomb flash; yet here and elsewhere, it seemed that the church had often not accepted its mission to the scientific community—had not, with the exception of Dr. Pollard and a sprinkling of others, tried to join and transform the people and things of science.

God would judge his church, as he always has. God was judging, right here in history, where the ticking quietness of nuclear piles sent no wisp of smoke into the air, and thousands of children flocked to the glittering halls of science. The church was being challenged and judged with each busload of children and each ton of nuclear explosives.

Let the judgment come, the poet breathed; let it winnow through the churches and seminaries, until God's church stands new and transformed in the bright, green dawn.

· 8 ·

Pretty Girl—and Beautiful Woman

THE poet walked along the tree-lined street with a few high school students, and one of them—a blond who filled her dress with shapely curves—kept with him as he walked. They breathed the evening air of the Kentucky bluegrass country, and saw the rim of an orange moon, as big as a dinner tray, rising over the fields' horizon.

But what did an evangelistic service have to do with this pretty blond on a spring evening? They were walking toward the Methodist Church in Millersburg, population 900 and surrounded by farmlands along dirt roads. The town had an integrated school, a military academy, and a single policeman whose main job was to run the dry cleaning shop. Here, in the church ahead, Miss Violetta Cavallero of Uruguay was to "bring the message" at an evangelistic service. What did the forty-year-old daughter of another country, short and heavily set, have to bring to this blond in the springtime of life, chattering about plans for "after graduation"? In the twilight, her beauty evoked passages from the Song of Solomon: "Who is this that looks forth like the dawn, fair as the moon. . . ."

"Bright he-he- blip futz. . . . "—this was the underlying effect of the girl's chatter. She was smart enough, and on the surface her words made sense. But underneath, there seemed to be some sort of confusion or dullness. The poet thought of that winsome and captivating blond, Marilyn Monroe, who beneath her beauty had been burdened with a load of problems and was dead now from too many sleeping pills.

"I think it would be nice to go there, sort-of interesting," the girl was saying. Yet her words were superficial, as though part of her was holding back, uncertain and shut in. It is a conspiracy, the poet mused ironically, in which he himself was joining with every advertisement and magazine to say, in effect, that the world should be all sunshine for a beautiful girl, that everything should go her way; and the beautiful girl felt this, and tried to live up to it, without even understanding what she was doing. Hence, she pushed her troubles and uncertainties down in her mind, where they festered, and her real self was fettered, unable to come to the surface—"and that would be kinda interesting too, hee-hee. . . . " she was saying.

Perhaps, he reflected, this conspiracy of admiration, focusing on the surface of a beautiful girl and making her live on the surface, is just as cruel in its way as joking at people who are awkward. They came now to the white clapboard church, and entered an interior shaped like a broad fan, widest at the back and narrowing somewhat toward the chancel area in the front. The pews and slightly raised chancel were made of dark wood, and faced each other in a broad confrontation.

The architecture spoke silently and thoroughly. It did not say what a Gothic design said: "We are drawing people up to God, via a clergyman and his doings at the altar." Rather, it said what the early American churches had said: "We gather people from the homes and farms, and meet together here, and confront each other across and through the reality of God."

The blond said good-bye and joined several girl friends in a pew two thirds of the way down the center aisle. The organ was being played, the service about to begin. The poet took a seat on the side, toward the front, and sat part-way around, so that he could see both the chancel, the pew of girls, and much of the congregation, simply by glancing rather than craning. The church was about half full for this special service. The blond had settled into one of her silences, looking straight ahead and blinking occasionally.

The Rev. William E. Parker, the pastor, announced the opening hymn. They stood, and sang all verses of "Blessed Assurance." They followed this by heartily singing all verses of another hymn. Then they were seated, with Miss Cavallero, the small choir and clergy occupying seats in the chancel. One of them was a visiting clergyman, who greeted the congregation and wound up by referring to the chunky Miss Cavallero as "Miss Uruguay."

There were smiles, quickly suppressed, in the congregation. The blond and her girl friends hid their faces behind handkerchiefs and pretended to cough, while the visible parts of their cheeks turned red and their shoulders quivered as they laughed. Miss Cavallero sat quietly in a chair in the chancel, her short and rounded figure clad neatly in a dress of subdued red with tiny black markings. She looked calmly at the visiting preacher, her face betraying no sign that she had heard his slip of the tongue or seen the reaction. So she weathered the moment, as she had doubtless weathered other such moments.

The service moved with a logic that drew the inner feelings of people, by alternating the gladness of song with the humility of prayer. So it moved toward the climax in the evangelistic message. Now Miss Cavallero rose to speak. She stood squarely in the front of the chancel, behind its low rail.

The congregation saw a fairly short, squarely—built woman with a large face and heavy limbs. The poet remembered Miss Cavallero telling him that afternoon: "When I was little I had a form of epilepsy that killed some others. Sometimes I would have fits and fall down, and roll over, though someone always watched me and kept me from being hurt." It may be that this had affected her physical growth.

Now, she was beginning to speak, her voice plain, with an undertone of resonance: "Have you forgotten? Don't you remember? Just at the end of the last war a young boy, coming back from the front, traveled all through your country with a great problem in his mind. Something in the war had made him forget everything that had happened to him and he was going from town to town seeking, asking anybody: 'Do you know who I am? Where I come from?' And do we—do we remember who we are? Have we forgotten where we come from?"

As she spoke the poet watched her and began to see, as it were, the words: the fine feeling-quality that came from her. In her native Montevideo, the doctors had predicted that she wouldn't survive puberty. They told her father that. Now she was speaking here, continuing the story of the lost young veteran:

"In city after city, as soon as he got off the train, the young man would begin to ask his questions and to see if anyone knew who he was. One day he appeared in a very little station with the same question. 'Is there anyone here who knows me? Who am I?' And among the few people at the station there came an elderly man with white hair, his eyes full of light, and stretching his hands toward the young man he said, 'You are my son!' And in that embrace and in that love the young man found himself and found his home.

"Have we forgotten?" Her question hovered in the still air of the church. "We walk through life many times and ask ourselves: Who am I? What am I here for? What is my relation with life and with eternity? And we may go walking through life until one day we don't find him; he finds us and he says, 'You are my son! I have given my life for you!' Yes, and do we remember. . . . "

The poet remembered that when Miss Cavallero was twelve, her father had told her the doctors' prediction that she might die fairly soon. And her father had said: "Beyond the doctors, there is God. Your mother and I have placed you in his hands. Whatever comes, Christ will be with you. You don't need to be afraid of anything. If you do live, you will belong to Christ in a special way." She had trusted her father and felt completely secure. Now, in the outlying Kentucky church, she was saying: "Do you remember who you are, whom you belong to? Have you forgotten the source of your love and power?" And her words went on, gently beating in the quiet air.

The girls in their pew had put their handkerchiefs away. Their faces were still, and their gazes were fixed on the speaking Miss Cavallero. There was a quiet silence in the face of the blond. With her face and figure, she would probably be married before long, joining the many women called to the ministry of patient and creative love, love that made a good home and strengthened a husband in his task, love that raised the next generation to carry the destiny of history and brotherhood and freedom on their shoulders. Would that blond be ready for such a mission? Did she know who she was? Could she begin to live from the deep source of love and power?

And Miss Cavallero was saying: "Through the Bible comes the word 'remember' as a golden thread. Remember, remember—why is this? Because we are so apt to forget. In life we *need* to forget, to be able to remember. What are the things we need to forget?

"I was traveling with another woman from Montevideo to Rio de Janeiro, with all the beautiful scenery of nature spreading before us, and at one place we stopped in a small town and had a cup of coffee. The coffee was quite cold. And for the rest of the trip, as we saw all the beautiful ways that God works in nature, the only thing that woman could remember was that little bit of cold coffee. She was not ready to remember the blessings because she was not ready to forget. We need to forget the cold coffee so that we can remember that God is interested in our whole lives, materially, intellectually, morally, spiritually. We are the ones who separate secular from spiritual.

"He has given us all things to enjoy. We need to forget the cold coffee and remember that he has given us ourselves and the love in our hearts, remember. . . . "

The poet remembered from the interview that Miss Cavallero's strange disease had begun to go away, soon after the talk with her father. Before long it was gone completely, against the doctors' predictions. There were no more seizures. She went on to be graduated from Crandon Institute, started by the church in Montevideo in 1879. She had obtained a higher education in the United States, and became a deaconess in her church. Now she directed religious education at Crandon, taught Bible classes, and counseled with students. The motto at Crandon was, "We learn to live when we learn to give." She was here on a temporary assignment, part of a mission to America.

"Do you remember," she was saying, "remember the first time you were in real true love and you decided to be the partner of that other person forever? What has happened to us that so many homes that have been built in the atmosphere of the church are broken today? Are destroyed? Have you forgotten that you promised love and understanding, to cherish the other? We leave even our own children without proper care, without proper love, and then wonder why teen-agers don't like to be in church. . . . "

The blond and her friends, motionless in their pew, showed neither like nor dislike, but simply calm and rapt attention. "What has happened?" Miss Cavallero was saying. "What has happened to your spiritual experience that we cannot share it, that you cannot give it? If we are not the mission, then we are the mission field. . . . "

Something rich and strange had been happening with Miss Cavallero, happening with and through her talking, through the whole feeling she created as she gave from herself. The poet had begun to see the inner person, the person who was weaving a spell with quite ordinary words, drawing the attention of everyone. And the person was beautiful.

"Do you remember only the surface of things?" she was saying. "In America you have so many, many material things. I'm glad I don't have so many things to take care of. It would make it harder for me to remember that God is interested in the whole person, interested in all of ourselves. . . . "

She provided an example in a story she told about a fifteen-year-old girl from a social center in Uruguay. The girl had begun coming to Miss Cavallero's office, and sitting on the blue couch or one of the two blue upholstered chairs. While Miss Cavallero worked at her desk the girl would sit, looking through magazines or sometimes staring out the window. Sometimes they exchanged a word or two. Miss Cavallero did not intrude. But when the girl left each time, saying, "Thank you," Miss Cavallero always said, "I wish I could do more." After about three weeks the girl opened up, and told Miss Cavallero about raging battles between her mother and father, with these fights centering on her. Miss Cavallero found an opportunity to talk with the parents and help them see the need for counseling. She gave them the name of a professional, and also counseled with the girl, who achieved a firmer sense of herself, and recognized that her parents were going through a difficult time.

Now the words of Miss Cavallero were hovering in the quiet air: "We say that Christ took the cross. We don't say that the cross was taking him. We can do that with our lives. We can let the crosses take us. But Christ took the cross—have we forgotten? We need to remember that with him there is strength and grace for all our lives. We need to remember that when God sends us he challenges us to show others the love that he gives us—the love we are given in our hearts. . . .

"The love that grows with the giving. For 'Lo, I am with you always, to the close of the age.' Have you forgotten? Do you remember?"

That was all. There was a long instant of silence as she turned away. Someone began to play the organ, and people who felt the inner need were urged to come forward and kneel at the low rail of the chancel. One of the first to come forward was the blond, quietly and soberly, perhaps a little dazed. The poet wondered if she knew what was happening—or if he himself knew, he mused. He would not sit in judgment. People were coming together, Miss Cavallero and different sorts of people and clergy coming together, through and around the reality of God. This was how it happened for a few minutes in a church in a small Kentucky town. It happened rather differently in a coffee house in the big city. But the experience would be fundamentally the same.

A little later, the service concluded and people went toward the rear doors as the organ played livelier music.

The poet put his notes in his folders and started for the doors behind the last of the little crowd.

On the steps of the church he found the blond, standing alone in the door light. The moon had risen higher among the tall trees, and a gentle breeze rustled the girl's hair. Across the road, car doors banged and motors whirred as people started home. The girl seemed lost in thought.

"Hello, there," the poet said.

"Oh, hi," and she gave him a smile.

"How are your plans?" he asked, pausing a moment, and alluding to her previous chatter.

She looked at him directly, her face calm and unashamed. "I've decided to be quiet awhile, and concentrate on school—give myself time to think."

In her words, the poet sensed some of the inner person, the person who was very young and unsure of herself and now remembered and faced these facts. The word that felt right for the moment came into his mind, and he said: "Remember . . . the beauty within?"

"Who?"

"Miss Cavallero—beautiful within, as a person."

"Why . . . yes, yes, she is."

That was all, though when the poet reached his rented car he could not resist turning to look. The church lights had gone out, and the girl stood silhouetted in the moonlight, her hair blowing softly in the breeze. She was looking at the blond moon, which seemed caught in the top of a tree and struggling to rise, like something within the girl herself.

· 9 ·

A Captain of Industry

THE huge beast of a trailer truck felt as though it would rock him off the highway as it roared past, doing an easy seventy. The poet veered right on route 31A. He drove through cold, sunny farmland, with signs: Mellons. Corn. Tomatoes. Fruit. A white roadside stand, tightly boarded, careened at the windshield and spun past. The poet slowed his rent-a-car to fifty. There came a roadside theater:

DRIVE-IN

FEATURING

CLOSED FOR WINTER

He was entering Columbus, Indiana, and the car lots and stores and "EAT" signs of highway culture were arrayed on all sides. He was going to interview a man who had made a roaring and finally a humming success of a thing that had so discouraged its German inventor, Rudolph Diesel, that in 1913 he had thrown himself off an English Channel steamer. The poet turned onto Washington Street, looking for 301, which he expected would announce itself boldly, as a tower of economic power in this town of 22,000. He watched the numbers, and soon he was coasting past two hundred something. So he swung around the block and parked. Obviously, he had missed 301. Just as obviously, 301 was inconspicuously but solidly there, because his man wouldn't be running several multimillion dollar businesses from a back room shack.

This was going to be the underplay, that classic style in American business, which came complete with dark suit and vest and surroundings of unpretentious excellence. The poet lunched at The Palms, a rather swank looking restaurant for Hometown, U.S.A. It had soft music and candles in little bubble jars on the tables. The menu offered a roast beef platter with vegetable, roll, and butter, for ninety cents, or a sausage platter with vegetable, roll, and butter, for eighty cents. He had the sausage—about a half pound piece. As he ate, he reflected that economic power wasn't wielded solely or even mainly by "Wall Street financiers" or "oil millionaires." It was diffused around the country. Real power, with leverage on the national economy, was headquartered down on that main street of a modest town on the Indiana flatlands, and here was wielded by a Christian who was a student of history and classical Greek.

The nerve center of power turned out to be an old, two-story brick building, its front screened by some iron grillwork and its interior completely modernized. The second floor reception room looked like a Greenwich Village apartment that had gotten itself all screwed together. There was even an abstract expressionist painting on the wall. Here, however, there was a deep carpet on the floor, and the form-fitting chairs not only had all their legs but were sumptuous.

He was a bit early and sat down to wait for his man, J. Irwin Miller, chairman of the board of the Cummins Engine Company; chairman of the board of the Irwin Union Bank and Trust Company; chairman of the board of the Union Starch and Refining Company; a director of the American Telephone and Telegraph Company; a director of the Equitable Life Assurance Society; a director of the Chemical Bank New York Trust Company; a director of Purity Stores of California; a trustee of the Ford Foundation, the Committee for Economic Development, and the National Industrial Conference Board; a fellow of the Yale Corporation; past president of the National Council of Churches; a member of this and that all over the country; the father of three girls and two boys, and. . . .

"Hello there," said Mr. Miller cheerfully, emerging from behind a polished, sliding wood panel at the end of the room. He stood more than six feet tall, had a salty grin on his lean face, and had kept all his hair, which was parted in big shocks of iron gray. He wore horn-rimmed glasses and a brown-black suit with a vest, and his tie was so conservative that it looked black, though on close inspection it showed narrow stripes. His handshake was firm. His eyes were deeply set and seemed a gun-metal blue.

As soon as they were seated in Mr. Miller's office, facing each other across the long table that served as his desk, with a log fire smouldering orange in a little fireplace at the end of the room, Mr. Miller began questioning the poet about the book. This wasn't just a defensive tactic, the poet felt. The fellow wanted to know what was happening and where he stood. So he told Mr. Miller. Then he turned the conversation into questioning, by taking hold of an inference about race relations.

"We have about a thousand Negroes here in Columbus," Mr. Miller replied. His voice had a Hoosier twang. His face was deeply lined, in a strong and sinewy way. "The schools are no problem," he was saying. "They've been integrated for a long time. But not all the industrial plants are open to Negroes, and we have some problem in higher income housing and hotels. Educated Negroes with good jobs have some difficulty getting the accommodations they want.

"But we're working at it," and he mentioned a municipal committee and other efforts. Mr. Miller indicated that he was working by persuasion, on a personal level, mostly with industrialists, to open up equitable employment for Negroes. Then he sat in silence, until prodded with further questions.

"Ideally, you just rule color out as a factor, one way or another," Mr. Miller responded. "But for a decade or so, I think we will have to give special encouragement to correct the balance. Until very recently, good white collar and management jobs simply haven't been available to Negroes. In the past year, more have opened up than there are Negroes to fill them. It's hard to find qualified Negroes because they haven't had any incentive to train and qualify. The doors have been closed. For a decade or so, until the balance is corrected, I think we'll have to go after

Negroes and encourage them." His lean jaw was firm as he spoke, and his tone was convinced and factual.

Now he lounged back in his desk chair, his legs crossed, and watched his interviewer intently from his deeply set eyes. This man didn't miss a trick. Behind him, there stretched a long, single bookshelf stacked with reference works, including the Holy Bible and Bartlett's *Familiar Quotations*. The wall back of the shelf consisted largely of windows which were entirely screened by heavy beige drapes. It was certainly a private office, and Mr. Miller was still silent, studying the poet.

From the uphill feeling of the conversation so far, and from his chance acquaintance with other captains of industry, the poet asked: "Why are businessmen apt to be so close-mouthed, or at least give this impression?"

Without flinching, Mr. Miller fielded the question directly: "As a businessman, you live in a world where people don't listen to you casually. Remarks can be taken with too much weight by others. Something you say may be interpreted as an indication of policy or a major decision. So you have to be careful. Also," he continued, taking off his glasses and still looking intently at the poet, "it is the fashion, part of the milieu and group thinking, just as it is the fashion for college professors to be liberal, and for ministers to be something else. Genuine independence of thought is one of the rarest qualities to come by. Everyone wants to be accepted by his group."

The poet narrowed his eyes slightly, and remarked, "I tend to go the other way, always questioning group thinking."

"I'm not sure of that. For instance, let's not kid ourselves. If we had lived in the Middle Ages, we would have shared their views—felt as they did about religion, the feudal system, and the rest. Similarly, we think in the fashion of today."

"Then don't you mean something deeper than fashion?"

"No, I mean fashion."

So that was that; the effort at discussion had fallen flat.

A moment later there came a buzz at the corner of the table-desk. Mr. Miller sat forward, lithe and alert. "This must be my call," he said briskly. "I'll take it in the other room."

"That's okay. I'll step out and stretch my legs," the poet replied.

"Fine," and as the poet got up, Mr. Miller picked the receiver off his call director telephone, roughly the size of a small portable typewriter, with push buttons and a retractable cord on the receiver. "Hello . . . yes . . ."

The poet went through the sliding panel and closed it behind him. From the newspapers, he knew that Mr. Miller was merging his Cummins Engine with White Motors. White, like Mack Truck and International Harvester, often used Cummins engines in their big machines because these engines were demanded by customers who wanted their outstanding performance. From his fistful of material—mainly magazine articles—the poet reviewed Mr. Miller's past.

J. Irwin Miller was a rich boy who had made good, the son of a wealthy family of industrialists and clergymen. He was born in Columbus in 1909, and grew up in the gloomy family mansion on its main street. He spent his childhood among articulate elders, and soon learned that he had better keep his mouth shut unless he had something important to say or ask. His father, the son of a preacher, made up such games as "name all the presidents in order by date." His Aunt Elsie, a spinster, wrote research papers on religious topics such as the different doctrines and methods of baptism. His grandmother was devoted to the social gospel approach in her faith, and made her adult Bible class something like a hiring hall for family businesses. His Uncle Will built a railroad, sold it at a nice profit when he foresaw the advance of highways and autos, and branched into the starch business. He also went into the engine business, pouring thousands and then hundreds of thousands of dollars into the work of Clessie Cummins, the genius mechanic who had started in a spare garage and was developing the engines that are named for him.

In this high-powered atmosphere, young Irwin had tended to be shy and had developed a stutter. He showed little talent for leadership or making friends. During his school years, the boys had liked to play on rich little Irwin's outdoor basketball court. But Irwin's only close friends had been the son of a carpenter and an orphan who cleaned spittoons at the Elks Club.

He went to Taft School and thence to Yale. From there, on the basis of his Latin and Greek studies, he was admitted to Balliol College at Oxford. He rowed on the college crew, began to gain confidence in himself, and lost his stuttering.

When he returned home, he was free to choose a career. Rather than entering the ministry, he felt a desire and obligation to carry on the family industries. To this, he brought a strong Christian concern, using his money and industries for the benefit of society. As he had put it to one interviewer, benefiting society is a man's main job. Otherwise, "Why are you taking up space?" He was given the Cummins Engine Company to manage. The starch industry and the chain of more than one hundred supermarkets came along in their time. It was with Clessie Cummins and his diesels that he learned business, by starting at the top and thrashing around in red ink.

But Cummins knew how to make a good engine, and the lean years of the 1930's developed a demand for the economical diesels. So Irwin developed the company, and Clessie was happy because he was free to work on his engines, and also had a nice chunk of stock that began to be profitable. Since the 1930's, under Mr. Miller's hand, sales have doubled about every five years. Early in the 1950's, the company was splitting 75 percent of the truck-diesel market with General Motors. Before the end of the 1950's, Cummins had 53 percent of that market, while General Motors had 7.5 percent. The power and standing of Cummins had continued to increase, and it had begun building turbodiesels that could sail fifty ton trucks along the superhighways.

By now, the poet reflected as he sat in the screwed-together Greenwich Village reception room, carpeted and elite, Mr. Miller had probably increased the family fortune to over 70 million dollars. He gave the deductable limit of his income to charity. He had married one of his former employees. He had good, liberal relations and policies with labor. He regarded a union not only as the right bargaining agent, but as a mirror to the company, reflecting its faults. A strong union, he had remarked to one person, helped him run the company better. He had raised wages and fringe benefits, introduced cost-cutting methods and machinery, and not only stayed ahead of the cost-price squeeze but forged ahead. Evidently he had moved ahead in business by being devoted to something bigger and finer than making money.

He had served as president of the National Council of Churches, and in a lot of other posts, and had represented his denomination, Disciples of Christ, in various national and international assemblies. He was a patron of the arts, owned and played a Stradivarius violin, and had been a good friend of the late Eero Saarinen, who had designed the Millers' vacation home on a Canadian lake, and had also designed a new building for the Irwin Union Bank and Trust Company in Columbus. Mr. Miller had noted in one religious magazine:

"People who say the church shouldn't 'meddle' in business or politics just don't understand the historic responsibilities of the church going back 2,000 years—and even farther, back through the Old Testament prophets. If Christianity is ultimate truth, as all Christians profess to believe, then our faith must be taken into account in every area of life. The church must continually produce new thinking about human conditions as these conditions change."

This was the man who was working behind the wood panels on a corporate merger. A moment later, the nearest wood panel slid aside and Mr. Miller invited the poet in again. The poet asked him how he did it: the Christian concern, benevolent ethics, and industrial success all rolled into one.

A Captain of Industry

Mr. Miller leaned back from the table, looked intently at the poet from his lean face, and began discussing the nature of responsibility. Then he went into the question of evolution, using examples from classical literature, human history, and even natural history. Survival and growth in human history, he declared, "require a considerable sense of responsibility to the whole. Too many societies have broken up because the ruling groups have wanted to preserve and foster their own interests apart from the welfare of the whole, or even against the welfare of the whole. We've got some of that in the South now." His eyes narrowed slightly on the poet, and he continued forcefully:

"For business, this means that you must pursue your industrial goals within the true interests of the community and the society. You can violate these interests for a while and get away with it. But if you violate the interests of society for too long, it will be the ruin of you and your business."

There was a quiet wisking sound, and his secretary, a charming woman dressed neatly in blue, emerged from behind a sliding panel with a tray of coffee. As the coffee was poured, Mr. Miller indicated that he was pressed for time and wouldn't have much longer for the poet. The poet was a bit worried by a calm finality conveyed by the words, even though Mr. Miller's letter had indicated that he would be in town for a couple of days. The poet had replied that he would appreciate a look at the Miller home and engine plant, and that he would stay in town for those days and make himself completely available, wherever and whenever Mr. Miller had time.

After the secretary left, the poet asked if he had coffee every afternoon.

"Yes, I guess it's the custom now," and he smiled slightly as he took a big sip.

Which reminded the poet, "Did you see *How to Succeed in Business Without Really Trying?*"

"Yes, I really *enjoyed* it," Mr. Miller responded heartily with a relaxed grin.

"That coffee-break sequence?"

"Wonderful," and they chuckled together over the Broadway comedy. This moment was the first time the poet had had a genuine dialogue with Mr. Miller, a real moment of give-and-take. But as they began discussing theology, their conversation went back to a series of interlocking monologues, like a couple of gear wheels that touched as they spun.

"If God created the universe," Mr. Miller was saying firmly, coffee cup in one hand, "then nothing is apart from him. We have to realize that the God of love is also the creator of polio, cancer, and earthquakes. We have to consider both aspects together. The universe stays in balance by a system of organized murder," and he cited certain fish and animals that are equipped simply to kill and eat.

"But," the poet finally asked, "what about evolution and responsibility, as you were saying earlier?"

"God created the situation in which men have to choose," he replied, looking intently at the poet from his deeply set eyes. "We even have to choose what to think about pain. And we always have to realize that we don't have final answers.

"In its whole import," his said, "the New Testament is not a set of ideal maxims. It says in effect: If you will look about you, and within yourself, you will see the operation of godly principles. Take the beatitudes. I think there are those who are pure in heart, who do see God with the intuition of the spirit. There are physical laws that govern the universe, and which we violate at our peril. I think there are laws governing the world of the spirit. We also violate these at our peril.

"For instance, it was Christ's custom to answer a question with another question, and often with a parable. So he finally made the person answer his own question. This has a very real implication. It means that the answers are within ourselves. We are being made to face the answers that we are born with. The same thing applies to the effective use of paradox and the unexplained parable. They rest on our having the answers within ourselves. We are being made to face these." The poet was just beginning to drink his coffee in a relaxed way, but noticed that Mr. Miller had finished his coffee with dispatch.

The questioning and replies swung to rebellion against the laws of the spirit, with Mr. Miller citing examples from Greek mythology. Then their talk went to the question of maturity and spiritual fiber. "I'm not at all appalled by the younger generation," Mr. Miller observed. "We hire and recruit a goodly number of youngsters every year from the colleges. They have been under a lot of competitive pressure to learn, and the ones who survive are pretty tough."

"Natural selection at a higher level?"

"Yes, and at a faster rate, moving more speedily. Life

is real and earnest to many of these youngsters, right in high school."

The poet sensed that it was time to go and got up. "When will I be able to see you next?"

"Perhaps in about a month, when I'm back in town," he replied with a brisk smile.

But I haven't seen his home or engines, the poet thought, remembering the exchange of letters. Yet, from Mr. Miller's manner, he was prepared for this. Still, he asked: "Is there any chance of having a look at your home tonight?"

"No, I'm sorry," Mr. Miller replied decisively, with a pleasant smile. "I have a lot of company business to catch up with, and I'm going right out of town on this merger."

They shook hands, and the poet thanked Mr. Miller for his time and for providing the written background material. As the poet walked out, he reflected that the truth of an interview with Mr. Miller was not the same as the infectious warmth of Paul Tournier in his home, nor the same as the graciousness of Sir Francis Ibiam, having someone show the poet around when he was busy with affairs of state. The truth of the visit with J. Irwin Miller, at this moment, was that he was under heavy pressure in his business schedule, was in the midst of merging two companies, and had to get on with this at once. He did not, as the poet half expected, ask to see what was written. The poet took this as an act of trust, rather than an oversight, because a man like Mr. Miller did not make oversights.

Outside, in the crisp sunlight of the Indiana afternoon, the poet reflected that it took many kinds of people to make a mission: varieties of gifts . . . varieties of service . . . one Lord. Men like J. Irwin Miller gave society its economic muscle, soundness, and ethics. For a moment, he looked up at the modern brick building with its heavily draped windows, wherein this man was merging two big corporations. That was his business. The poet turned and strolled away with a carefree step, confident that Mr. Miller was using his industrial power to give effect to sound Christian ethics and to benefit the commonweal.

· 10 ·

A Creative Woman

SHE was wearing a simple dress in a flowery pattern, and her dark hair spilled across her shoulders as she knelt on the grass and leaned forward, weeding the little flower border beside her neat suburban ranch house. Her pastor had arranged the interview. It was agreed that she would be frank, and he wouldn't use her name—which might as well have been Mrs. Smith, because she lived in a commonplace house in a commonplace suburb, like a million other young women.

She was quite an attractive young lady. The poet noticed this as she stood, dusted her hands against her skirt, and came forward to greet him, her pug nose crinkling slightly with a smile. Hers was not a dolled, cosmetic gesture at sexiness. Her only visible makeup was a trace of lipstick. Her clothes were not tight, she wasn't markedly pretty, and she was modestly proportioned. But from her sandled toes to the top of her simply-combed hair, in her easy manner and every gesture, she was thoroughly and attractively female—the kind of woman a man enjoyed being near.

They settled down with coffee on the little back terrace, after moving a tricycle and a set of dolls to one side. The two older children were at school, and the youngest was napping inside.

"Dr. Stichman tells me you've been raising quite a ruckus," the poet began.

"Really? I've simply been talking about being a woman."

"As wife and mother. . . ."

"Yes, and it began in confusion—total chaos!" she replied with pleasing feminine exaggeration. "But seriously," she continued, "look how far people have gotten from the simple facts of womanhood. After Dan—he's my husband—got his break with the company, and we settled here, I found a lot of the girls were—well, just whirling around. They were rushing between children and husbands and meetings at church or school, and some of them wanted to go back to work to use their education. They were all so . . . *busy*.

"You know," she continued, "my father—he ran a grocery store in Vermont—he used to tell my sister and me: 'If you hear a lot of noise, don't jump on the tracks. You'll likely get hit by a train.' Well, I saw all this noise around here, and instead of jumping into it, I took a long look and had a long think. It seemed to me that a lot of these women were chasing life, as though they could catch it if they ran fast enough. But does someone find happiness that way?"

She let the question hang, studying the poet. "And this

led you," the poet suggested, "to the question of what it means to be a woman."

"Yes, and it suddenly hit me, that the women we hear most about are the exceptions and odd-balls. You go to the movies, and the leading woman character is usually some siren, or neurotic, or some sort of desperate female who's headed off the deep end. You look at the fashion magazines, and you see one skeletal model after another, wearing extreme, exotic clothes and layers of makeup. And every so often, the magazines pop up with articles bemoaning the fact that we're 'merely' housewives and mothers"—her voice was caustic with sarcasm—"and they tell us to go to work at some desk or laboratory because our precious talents are being wasted. That really makes me burn! I suppose you have to be an uneducated slob to be a housewife." She was talking avidly now, tossing out the words.

"Then there's the church. I've always been a member of some church—I was brought up that way. So I talked with Dr. Stichman, and you know what he said? He said I could teach Sunday school, and join the Ladies Missionary Guild, and help with a Thursday meeting. I told him I'd teach Sunday school—do one job. But where did I have time for all the rest, if I was going to be a good wife and mother? It was nearly the last straw.

"I came home and lay on the bed. Fran—a friend of mine—was keeping the baby, and I had about an hour before the others got home from school. So I lay there, and I remembered how it had been that morning with Dan and me."

"How do you mean?"

She smiled demurely, and replied: "I don't think a woman should be clinical and explicit about everything, unless she needs help from a pastor or doctor."

"How come?"

"The Bible uses the word *knowing*. Through sex, a man and wife *know* each other, in the deepest sort of way—or a least they should. I think people run into trouble when they make sex less than it is—a form of recreation, or a blind compulsion. But the Bible word—*knowing*—is the right one. And you can't describe this with a lot of physical mechanics."

"The marriage manuals do," the poet pointed out.

"Yes, and my first advice to a young married couple would be to throw them out. Sure, people *should* have a sound knowledge of their bodies. But the manuals are full of saying that a man should do this, and a woman should do that, and feel thus and so—a lot of technical directions. For my money, technology belongs in the kitchen." The poet chuckled, and the woman skipped ahead, pouncing on a new example:

"Look at that novel, *The Group*. Its whole approach to sex is clinical . . . and sadistic in a semi-disguised way. The women in it needed psychiatrists, not lovers, because they didn't show the faintest notion of love—not the faintest! Oh, I know the book was well-written—brilliantly written, I guess. But there have also been brilliant murders committed."

"You'd ban the book?"

"No, I'm not for censorship, or anything like that. But why not call a spade a spade? Why not say that a good part of the book is a cold-blooded murder of sex? I remember my grandmother, on the farm. She was pretty straight-laced, the way she often talked to my sister and me. I'd guess you'd call her a puritan, and puritanism is out. I wouldn't want to bring it back. But I'll say one thing: Grandma was never *vicious* about sex."

She took a sip of her coffee. "Is this some of what you thought that morning in the bedroom, after seeing Dr. Stichman?" the poet prompted.

"Well, partly. I thought of Dan with me that morning, when we woke up, and then how he went to work with a spring in his step and a great feeling of confidence. And I knew," she added with a cat-like expression, "where his buoyant feelings came from. Then I looked down at the end of the bed. There was a little pile of shirts that I'd ironed for Dan, after he left for work. They were ready for him to pack for a business trip he was taking the next day.

"You know," and she smiled a bit coyly at the poet, "you men have a lot of idiosyncracies. For instance, the way the laundry does shirts isn't good enough for Dan, at least when he's going on a trip. So I do them for him, and it makes a difference in how he feels. So does the fact that I cook and serve him breakfast, and put on a clean dress for him at night. These things make a real difference in the way he feels and looks at life—and I think in his performance. All the things a woman does, as a love partner to a man, add up to quite a difference in a man's life and career. A woman can break a man or do a lot to bring out his potential."

"It sounds like a man is pretty dependent on his wife."

"Yes and no. The results come by a woman depending

on her man, in the right way—depending on him to wear the pants in the house, and bring home the paycheck, and be a good father to the children. Well, take those shirts I iron. He depends on me for those. But I depend on him wanting them, and on my work making a difference for him.

"And of course," she continued, "I thought a lot about the children that morning. I thought of all the noses I'd wiped, and all the meals I'd cooked, and all the diapers I'd changed, and the bedtime stories I'd told—the whole bit, and how each thing was important.

"Then—"and her voice took an edge of excitement— "I remembered watching a sidewalk artist, one time, as he painted a picture. He put on a dab of this color, a stroke of that, and a line of something else. I thought of that, and suddenly my life made sense. I was doing the same thing as the artist, only much more so, because I was doing it with real lives. He was using paint to make a picture. I was using my femininity, and household, and kitchen, and food, and clothing and all the rest—to create a living climate, a psychological environment. And the way I created this, or failed to, made a lot of difference to Dan, and made all the difference in the world to our children.

"Well, I've done a lot of living and thinking since that day two years ago, and I've seen the ideas at work. For instance, our middle child wants to go overseas as a missionary for the church. I don't know if he will or not. Dan and I would be very proud if he did. But will he understand the people he serves? It depends a lot on whether I give *him* understanding, and create a basis for his understanding others. And is he going to love others, in a real and effective way? I think he will, if Dan and I create in him the love and strength and freedom, by the way we love him. This is something that begins very early, and it's mainly a woman's job to think about it—because Dan thinks mostly of his career.

"Or take our daughter—our oldest. Already, in fifth grade, she's running into talk about sex and dances. My gosh, some mothers around here are trying to rush their girls into young womanhood before they've had any girl-hood! And that's just the beginning. In the paper the other day, I read that promiscuity and illegitimate preg-nancies are steadily increasing among high school and col-lege girls. And why do the girls get pregnant, with all this modern knowledge of birth control? The psychologist, who was writing the article, said they had unconscious needs for doing so. Sure! The Bible speaks about *knowing*. A woman wants to know a man, and be known—wants to give herself, and bear his children, and create a home. This is what her feelings mean, which is why she shouldn't give her womanhood away cheap.

"Grandma used to tell my sister and me: 'Gather ye rosebuds while ye may—but don't give away the basket until you're settled with the right man.' Our daughter will need to understand this. It isn't any good just telling her 'no! no!' It should be 'yes! yes!' with a wedding band on. Or, if she isn't going to marry, she will have to under-stand how to fulfill her womanhood as a single woman."

"You're not ruling that out?"

"Of course not! My third grade teacher was a marvelous person! And she never married. Anyway, our daughter will need all the inner strength and love and savvy that can be created in her.

"So," she said with a smile, recrossing her pretty legs, "it comes down to something obvious and tremendous. Being a wife and mother isn't simply a thing-to-do. Women in our shoes mainly create the things—the feelings, the psychology, and the rest—by which children will carry forward their faith, and shoulder the destiny of civilization. And this," she said with a quiet understatement, "is very important. It means the future of mankind. We create its basis, in our homes and back porches. For this, a woman uses all the education she has."

"Is that your main resource?"

"Womanhood, faith, education—in that order. The womanhood is given, and Christianity lets me understand *how* I use this as a wife and mother—the self-giving and creativity in daily life. Education gives me the means."

"Can you give an example?"

"Sure. My college art courses have been important. I don't mean the techniques. I mean something deeper— the understanding of harmony, form, creativity and the like. I use some of this in interior decoration, creating effects and moods. But mainly it's a matter of tone. A painter uses different tones. Well, there is something called 'emotional tone.' People have emotional tones—feelings, their pitch and quality. For instance, you know what a *shrill* household is like?"

"Yes. Does that mean not enough sweetness and light?"

"Partly, though sweetness and light can be a trap. You have to blow off steam. After all, a husband can get on your nerves, and children can fray them raw. And unless you blow off steam, everything will get depressed. But there's a right way of blowing off steam, a way that clears the air and makes for better understanding, and shows the kids that they can blow off steam too, in the right way. Of course, I'm using some of what I learned in psychology, though I wish I'd had better courses."

"What did you have?"

"Elementary psychology, which tells about nerve patterns and putting rats through mazes. Then I took educational psychology, which is great for teachers, and I had abnormal psychology, which is dandy if you're planning to marry a psychotic."

They laughed, and she added: "Seriously, those courses have been a help. But it would be better if college offered a normal psychology, geared for women who are going to be wives and mothers. After all, this is what most of us do. Later, when the kids go to college, I'll probably join the Ladies Missionary Guild, and do volunteer work at the hospital. I'm all for it! And I think a woman who has learned her womanhood by being a wife and mother can bring a lot to those jobs.

"But I won't forget that my life is still basically here, with Dan as my husband. By that time, he'll probably be reaching the point in his career where he'll either stand still for the rest of his life, or he'll show that extra something that he needs to give his best. And I think I can make the difference, by being a good love partner."

"Paul said that we're all one—neither Jew nor Greek, male nor female."

"Yes, which means we're treated equally by God. Sex or culture or race or whatever doesn't count for us or against us. But we aren't desexed or deGreeked by being Christian. Dan functions *through* his manhood. I work *through* my *womanhood.*"

"Which probably explains," the poet rejoined, "why you have become such a feminine person."

She smiled prettily, her pug nose crinkling, and then said, "I'm still not sure why you wanted to interview me. Aren't you writing about missionaries?"

"About mission in daily life. I think it begins with experiences of God's grace, and love, and liberating strength —which usually come *through* someone. So I want to thank you," he said, rising to leave, "for telling me about the creative ministry of womanhood."

· 11 ·

The Poet's Chapter

AFTER all his interviews and writing, the poet thought of trying to summarize the experience and its lessons. But he decided not to, because he isn't a preacher, and he believed that the power of personal example in each chapter spoke for itself. Rather, as he sat at the window of his apartment, he affirmed his own way of expressing Christianity—his variety of gift, his form of mission—and wrote a poem.

The Presence of Christ

I found you in the hurrying winds
where evening doorlights were prismed in streets
and blown newspaper told of worn-out wars.

I found you in the hurrying crowds
that throng the long Broadways of my mind,
muttering of lightning and blood—
the pale sparks of storms broken and dying.

The Poet's Chapter

I found you in the gray raindrops of desolation,
and discovered you in the fire of a thousand dawns
where lilacs rustle the swift spring.

I found you in the sky's tall sea
and felt you in the deep dancing of silences
of my unknown mind. I found you, and gazed
amazed, to see your love had found me.

A WORD ABOUT THE FORMAT

The text of this book is set in Caledonia, 11 point leaded 2 points. Designed by the late W. A. Dwiggins, this linotype face belongs to the "modern" family of type faces and is somewhat similar to Scotch Modern, although more freely drawn than that letter.

Manufactured by Sowers Printing Company, Lebanon, Pa. Jackets and paper covers by Affiliated Lithographers, Inc., New York
Paper: S. D. Warren's Olde Style Wove
Typographic design by Margery W. Smith
Binding design by Louise E. Jefferson